15-10-99

CW00543685

The Ai

from

Trigger

to

Target

G.V. Cardew & G.M. Cardew

ISBN 0 9505108 2 3

First Published August 1995

Reprinted June 1996

W.H. SMITH LTD
HIGH WYCOMBE
TELEPHONE NO: 01494 525011
V.A.T.   238 5548 36
Thank You For Shopping With Us
Cashier: TILL 5

                                      £
AVD PAYMENT BOOKS   14.99

1 BAL DUE   14.99

CASH   20.00
CHANGE   5.01

3918 007 05 8642 12:12 25SEP99

The Airgun from Trigger to Target
G.V.Cardew & G.M.Cardew

ordered

CONTENTS

The Air Gun from Trigger to Target

Contents

Contents

ACKNOWLEDGEMENTS

No book of this complexity can be written by two people working totally on their own, they both need plenty of support from family, friends and the airgun industry. Our wives Kath and Sally-Anne, also our families had a lot to put up with especially when we were doing noisy experiments, or using the garden as a shooting range; we must thank them for their patience.

We owe a deep debt of gratitude to Robert Hull, it was he who built all the chronographs for Cardew Air Rifle Developments (CARD). He also built the specialist electronic equipment so vital to our investigations; without electronics the accurate study of airguns is impossible.

Our thanks must go also to Helical Springs Ltd. of Lytham for passing a professional eye over the chapter on springs, they were able to put us right on the details of spring making which has made that chapter more interesting.

Special thanks must go to Mr. Miles Morris who came to our rescue when we wrote the chapter on pellet flight. Miles is a professional ballistician who has worked on the flight problems of everything from missiles to pellets, he is also a keen airgunner.

Thanks are owed to our friend and colleague Roy Elsom who helped with advice on many occasions, but principally for his help with the chapter on recoil.

Recognition must also go to John and Janet Eades of Olton, Birmingham, who helped us with the photography.

Manchester Air Guns must also be thanked for obtaining odd barrels and other parts for our experimental equipment.

A final thankyou must go to Kath who, although being a non technical person, bravely proof read the final manuscript.

We are also indebted to Mr. J.B. Forster of Runcorn who sent us instructions for catching pellets in polyester fibre.

FOREWORD

When in 1976 we wrote *"The Airgun from Trigger to Muzzle"* we were fully aware that it was not a *full* investigation into the phenomena attached to spring rifles, let alone the problems associated with pneumatic guns in their various forms. We determined, after publication, to continue our quest for the truth about these strange machines. As the search progressed and many new facts came to light, we realised the merit of the old saying: *"Nothing improves until someone stops and questions an accepted belief"*. This is because we often found that some of the old accepted beliefs attached to airguns were totally wrong. Probably the most outstanding example being, *"That a longer barrel on a gun increases its velocity"*. This may well be true in the case of a firearm, but holds little truth in the case of a spring gun.

The present work covers a far greater field than the previous, embracing both the study of pneumatics and the flight of the pellet. At the same time we can now describe why a spring gun may operate in any one of *"four phases"*, depending upon a multiplicity of factors. It is the appreciation of these four phases which provides the key to the understanding and management of spring guns and their often erratic performance.

Although a spring gun at first appears to be a very simple system, its action is in fact far more complicated than that of a pneumatic. There are many factors influencing the performance of a spring gun, and very often the alteration of on will upset the others, so its design becomes a matter of balance and compromises. On the other hand the factors which influence the performance of a pneumatic are well understood and controllable, alteration of any one element will usually bring about the expected result without upsetting the others.

Since 1976 there has been an explosion in airgun designs and systems, each new gun being built to satisfy a particular demand in the market place. This diversity has resulted in the old saying, *"there are horses for courses"* becoming totally applicable to guns. It is no longer possible to name the *best* air gun without accurately declaring its purpose, what might be the ultimate in one situation could be next to useless in another.

In this book little mention will be made of air pistols, this is because they were seldom used in experiments but their performance and characteristics are exactly the same as those of a rifle, only scaled down. Also, the word *"weapon"* will not be used. We consider this name to be derogatory to airguns, implying violence and suggesting savagery !

Chapter 1
INTRODUCTION

Most airgun enthusiasts start off with a spring gun and then perhaps go on to own a pneumatic. With this thought in mind spring guns would seem to be the obvious starting point for a book on air guns.

It is a surprising thing that very often a subject which appears on first sight to be very simple, often, on further study, turns out to be very complicated. This statement is exceptionally true when applied to the spring air gun, as we found out when we first began to investigate the subject many years ago.

The trouble all started with a small 'barrel cocker' that we bought second hand. Generally it would perform very well and give successively accurate shots, then for no apparent reason the pellets would go high or low, causing much frustration. Being scientifically minded and curious we decided to try to improve on the original construction by making the breech seal a better fit. The cylinder was polished and the sear refitted. Each alteration and adjustment helped, but the real reasons behind the problems still remained obscure.

More rifles were looked at and some bought so that we could examine them and check their performance. In each case we measured what we considered, at the time, to be their "vital dimensions", by this procedure we hoped to be able to spot why one type of rifle was better than another. But it soon became clear that physical dimensions alone were not going to be the answer, there must also be other areas to be investigated.

In those early days accurate electronic chronographs were not available and we had to rely on our own home built ballistic pendulums to tell us how fast our pellets were travelling. But pendulums are slow and cumbersome to use, so we built a sound operated electronic chronograph from old computer parts; the sound at the muzzle and the noise of the pellet hitting a steel plate providing the start and stop pulses. This simple instrument was the forerunner of a line of light operated chronographs, which were sold both to airgunners and industry in the years to come.

By this time we were utterly and completely committed to the solution of the problems of spring guns and why so little of the energy in the spring appears in the pellet as it leaves the muzzle. As our interest in airguns developed we searched the library shelves for a book that might help us, but the space was empty, this work is aimed at filling that space. We hope that in the following chapters the reader will find the answers to his own particular questions; also he will be better able to understand the physics involved in his gun.

Perhaps the most fundamental question that must be asked is: "Why use air at all ?" After all, a bow projects an arrow without air and also a catapult can fire a stone. Perhaps the air adds energy to the pellet, or is needed because a gun has a barrel whereas a catapult does not. No, the air is only a medium used to couple the heavy, relatively slow moving piston to the light fast-moving pellet. It is this great difference between the mass of the driving force and that of the projectile which makes a coupling medium necessary.

Physics is a subject full of graphs, so the reader must accept them as a necessity in a book of this nature. The first one that we shall use **fig 1.1** relates three factors, pellet weight, pellet velocity and pellet energy. One of the chief uses of this diagram is to compare two rifles of different calibres, but it can also be used to compare pellets of different weights fired from the same rifle. It makes these comparisons possible by providing the means of converting weights and velocities to that all important figure, the "muzzle energy". Muzzle energy is the term which describes the output power of a gun, neither velocity nor projectile weight are adequate terms on their own, they must be combined together before the power of the gun can be defined.

The muzzle energy of an air rifle is the figure normally used in legal terms to determine whether or not the gun should be classed as a firearm. At the present time in England restrictions are placed on rifles that can exceed 12 Foot Pounds of muzzle energy, and on pistols which can exceed 6 Foot Pounds. These figures were laid down in 1969 at a time when few rifles or pistols could achieve these energies, since then however, technology has caught up with the law and now most rifles are easily capable of these powers.

Over the years, manufacturers and sportsmen have always spoken of, and perhaps boasted about, the velocity of their favourite rifle. While this may be quite reasonable in advertisements or in the bar of the "Red Lion" it has little place in physics, for no mention has been made of the weight of the projectile. It is rather like telling your friends that you can travel at 50 miles per hour. This in itself is not remarkable at all, until you carry on to mention that you do so by

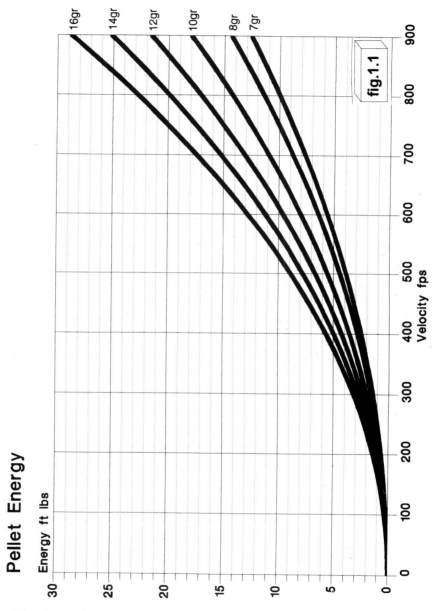

Pellet Energy

fig.1.1

bicycle or steam roller ! Weight is just as important as speed, a fact that is easily overlooked.

In order to determine the energy of any projectile, it must first be weighed and then the velocity at which it is travelling measured. Normally the velocity reading is taken within six feet or so of the muzzle, at this point the projectile is at its maximum velocity and the muzzle blast that follows the projectile has minimal effect on the measuring instruments.

These two factors, weight and velocity, can then be substituted in Newton's well-known equation for kinetic energy, that is the energy possessed by a moving body.

$$E = \frac{1}{2}MV^2$$

Where E = Energy, M = Mass, V = Velocity.

But since we are dealing here with weight and not mass we must convert the equation into:

$$E = \frac{WV^2}{2g}$$

Where W = weight and g = the acceleration due to gravity. Which in this book will be taken as 32.16 FPS^2. This will give us the kinetic energy which that projectile contains when it travels at velocity V.

Suppose that we wish to determine the energy in Ft.lbs. of a pellet weighing 14.5 grains that is travelling at a velocity of 500 FPS. We must first apply the above equation where; W = 14.5 Grains, V = 500 FPS, g = 32.16 FPS^2. To convert grains to pounds we have to divide by 7000. (There are 7,000 grains in a pound). Thus **E = 8.05 Ft.lbs.**

It is well worth spending a bit of time here considering what a foot pound really is. It is obviously made up of two common terms, a foot being a unit of length and a pound being a unit of weight, when these two are combined together a unit of energy results. The blunt statement is that one foot pound is the amount of energy required to lift a one pound weight one foot off the floor.

Chapter 1 - Introduction

When one pound weight is supported one foot above the ground, it is said to contain one foot pound of potential energy. In other words it contains one foot pound of energy which can be employed at some future time. If, on the other hand it is released and falls to the ground its potential energy will be converted into kinetic energy as it drops, which will probably be absorbed by making a dent in the floor !

This energy must not be confused with what we humans might consider to be work; for one of us to stand for an hour with a twenty pound weight in each hand would be hard work indeed. Yet in the world of physics we would merely be supporting weights and would not be doing any work at all, at least not in the terms of Newton's laws.

Of course in air gunning we never have to deal with something so simple as weights falling to the ground, we are interested in pellets flying more or less horizontally. However Newton's laws may still be used to obtain the kinetic energy of our pellets because they are only small weights, but this time moving horizontally.

We have found throughout our work with spring air rifles that the overall mechanical efficiency of an "average gun" that is not burning oil, is about 30%. That is for every foot pound of the energy stored in the compressed spring only one third of a foot pound will appear in the flying pellet. The reasons for this inefficiency have been investigated and will be discussed in the following chapters. However, in order to start understanding the working of an air rifle, one must know the sequence of events inside the gun, for instance, does the pellet start at the moment of peak pressure ? Does the piston stop before or after the pellet leaves the muzzle ? etc.

The sequence was established by making the various components of the gun such as the piston and pellet interrupt light beams which in turn produced electrical pulses to be displayed on an oscilloscope **fig 1.2**.

The piston starting, the piston stopping, the pellet starting and the pellet leaving the end of an eighteen-inch barrel each produced a pulse on the top trace of the oscillogram. The only negative pulse (downward going) on the trace is that of the piston stopping. The lower trace shows the pressure rise inside the cylinder as measured in this instance by an uncalibrated transducer.

The first positive pulse is that from the piston starting after the trigger is pulled, the second is from the pellet as it starts off up the barrel, the third positive pulse is that produced by the pellet leaving the muzzle and the fourth pulse (negative) is that of the piston finally stopping at the end of the cylinder.

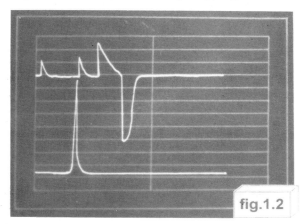

fig.1.2

So summarising the above sequence; the piston starts, the pellet then starts, (notice that this happens at the point of peak pressure), the pellet then leaves the barrel and the piston comes to rest against the front end of the cylinder soon after. We will show in a later chapter that in fact, the piston comes very close to the end of the cylinder at the moment of peak pressure, but then rebounds backwards off the high pressure air cushion in front of itself.

It must be borne in mind throughout this book that everything happens at very high speed. For instance, the time base of the oscillogram, i.e. the length of the horizontal line is equivalent to 50 milliseconds (ms), that is, fifty thousandths of a second. Thus the total time from the start to the stop of the piston is about $1/3$ of 50 ms i.e. 17 ms This is shown by the fact that the cycle of events is completed in the first third of the trace. (In this time a pellet travelling at 500 FPS would have covered a distance of eight and a half feet !)

Also, in most of the chapters the reader will find there are conflicting effects that an alteration of an individual component can have on the final performance of the rifle. The balancing of these factors will be discussed in the chapter on Tuning, but these variations are responsible for the fascination which the spring gun holds for airgunners.

Chapter 2
THE FOUR PHASES

As we said in the last chapter, the spring gun is a very complicated machine. Although at first sight it might appear to be purely a spring operated air pump mounted on a wooden stock - nothing could be further from the truth. For instance, in our early studies we accepted that the oil we used purely lubricated the works, unless excessive amounts were applied, in which case the gun dieselled. We also accepted what then appeared to be a common sense attitude, that if the spring power was increased then obviously the velocity of the pellet must also improve; or if we polished the cylinder to reduce friction the velocity would increase. As time went on and our experience from working on many rifles grew, we began to realise that in fact what we often thought was the obvious road to the improvement of a gun's performance was actually the very opposite. It was a bit like viewing life in a mirror, everything was reversed.

One or two big disappointments forced us to take stock of what we knew and what we were trying to do, that brought us to the conclusion that the whole problem was far more complicated than we had imagined and it was suggested that in fact any spring gun could operate in any one of four distinct phases; these we called the **Blowpipe**, the **Popgun**, the **Combustion** and the **Detonation** phases. Application of this theory offered answers to many of the difficulties we had encountered, especially why identical models of the same rifle could produce such widely differing powers depending on variable factors such as lubrication or pellet fit. In subsequent years we have always found the theory to be sound, problems with the performance of spring guns, when analyzed in this light, have been solved. Or if not solved, then the reason why not, has become clear.

Phase I - Blowpipe

The first phase we christened the *Blowpipe* phase because the gun performs in a similar fashion to a native blowpipe, the projectile must be a slack fit in the barrel so as to allow the reduced air pressure to move it along the bore. This phase is normally only employed by relatively low powered guns and pistols firing the old fashioned cat slugs or perhaps steel BB balls. The BB firing gun is seldom rifled and the ball is not tight in the barrel, in fact it is usually held in the breech prior to firing either by a light spring or a magnet to prevent it from falling out along the barrel.

Since the ball is not a tight fit in the breech or barrel of the BB gun, it therefore provides no seal, the piston is unable to build up pressure it before it starts off and the final velocity is relatively low. In these lower powered pistols and some early rifles too, the pellet had to be seated a short distance into the bore, either by a separate tool or by part of the gun itself. The idea of this was to ensure that no spring energy was lost in forcing tight pellets into the bore, but more importantly to ensure that the gun would actually fire them!

In the market for very low powered junior rifles or pistols capable of firing standard lead pellets the employment of the *blowpipe phase* is the only way in which a reasonable degree of success is likely to be attained. Early pellet firing rifles of this type were mainly of the "tinplate" variety which have now just about vanished from the scene, except for those designed especially for the firing of BB balls. Of course fairground rifles firing darts are still an important aspect of this phase. The latest craze of "Soft Airguns" employs this phase, these fire lightweight plastic balls from imitation firearms. However, little more will be said in this book about the *blowpipe* phase because it is not of any serious technical interest. If the cylinder were large enough and the barrel long enough, the oversize gun might have acceptable characteristics - which leads us nicely to the next paragraph.

Mention must be made of the native weapon. This is probably the most interesting, efficient and sophisticated example of a system for firing a projectile by air that we know. The calibre, weight and shape of the dart have evolved by trial and error over centuries to perfectly match the length of the blowpipe and the power and capacity of the owner's lungs. The result is a wonderful system upon which the hunter relies for his food, and therefore his life and the lives of his family too. It is made for serious hunting, certainly not as a pastime. The manufacture of the pipe itself is a marvel of workmanship and skill, especially when one considers the lack of facilities. The pipe's length and calibre must be correct so that the shooter can maintain a constant pressure behind the moving dart as it is accelerated up the tube. Though one can only presume that over the years the owner's lungs develop extra strength, in much the same way as those of a modern glassblower.

Phase II - Popgun

The *popgun phase* is best described as the condition within the gun where the pellet is firmly held at the start of the bore and no combustion of lubricant occurs when it is fired. We have, perhaps, picked an unfortunate name for this phase; nobody likes to think of his expensive match rifle as being a popgun. Yet no other name describes so accurately a gun working without the aid of combustion. This phase lends itself to precise physical analysis better than all the others, and indeed was the subject of our previous work "The Airgun from Trigger to Muzzle." Each component in the system will be discussed and analyzed in future chapters together with observations on their effect in other phases. A rifle working within this phase produces shots of very consistent velocity but of lower velocity when compared with those where combustion of the lubricant occurs. For successful operation within the popgun phase the various components of the gun must be designed and shaped to suit that phase, for instance the entry to the barrel must be a polished radius so as to ensure the pellet releases at the correct point in the piston's stroke every time. Also the piston's seal must be very good so that no oil or grease passes it as the gun is cocked.

Spring guns designed for high level competition shooting work in this phase and are capable of producing shot to shot velocity variations of only a couple of FPS. However owners are often disturbed by the instruction that no oil must be applied to the working parts, this instruction ensures that no excess lubricant is present to pass the piston's seals where it will burn and therefore change the gun's consistency.

The term *popgun* was given to this phase because when the trigger is pulled the piston rushes forward, increasing the pressure of the air in front of it and therefore behind the pellet also, until sufficient pressure has built up to unstick the pellet and force it along the barrel; in much the same manner as the cork flies out of a popgun once the pressure behind it has reached a critical point. Inevitably, of course, the air is heated by the compression and therefore expands to further increase the pressure behind the pellet before it leaves the breech. However, the air cools again and loses pressure as it expands behind the moving pellet and the energy gained from the heating is lost, leaving the pellet with only the energy it obtained from the spring to drive it along.

As an interesting piece of history, in 1814 a firearms inventor called Samuel Pauley took out a patent for a system by which the powder in his cartridges was ignited by a blast of air heated by violent compression in a tiny cylinder by a spring-loaded piston.

Phase III - Combustion

The *combustion* phase is the phase in which most high powered sporting spring rifles operate. As the piston comes forward on firing, the temperature of the air in front of it rises with the pressure; this very high temperature causes oil, or any other combustible substance to burn, thereby increasing the pressure further, producing enough energy to drive the pellet up the barrel at a very high velocity. Since the combustion relies on the high temperature created by the compression we originally called this phase the "Diesel engine phase". However, this led to complications with the next phase, and since it is a bit of a mouthful anyway it came to be known by its present, more descriptive, name.

Because the final pressure in the barrel depends on the quantity and characteristics of the lubricant present also the replenishment of this fuel, the cycle is somewhat erratic and unpredictable. The final velocity may not be as consistent as in the popgun phase, but this lack of consistency is of less importance when shooting vermin at long ranges. Like so many other characteristics of air guns, a compromise has to be struck between two or more conflicting requirements.

Phase IV - Detonation

Finally, the *detonation* phase. This is a very difficult phase to study because it is a phenomenon which seldom occurs, but when it does the results can be disastrous. To experiment with it is risking permanent damage to the rifle. As we understand it, it would seem that if a certain critical quantity of lubricant is present in front of the piston when the rifle is fired, normal combustion will take place; but then this combustion will in turn set off a chain reaction in the remainder of the fuel and it will detonate. Detonation is an instantaneous rearrangement of molecules which occur at very high temperatures and pressures - as it happens large amounts of energy will be released. A good example of a detonation is when a toy cap is struck. Energy in the form of heat, light and sound are all produced by the instantaneous expansion of the gasses. Our observations indicate that ambient temperature influences the occurrence of detonations in air rifles, they may occur more readily on hot days than on cold, depending on the lubrication employed.

Looking at firearms for a moment, a substance which detonates is useless as a propellant, though of course a small amount is necessary in every cartridge to set off the propellant. But if a cartridge were to be fully charged with a detonant on its own without the normal propellant, the gun would be destroyed because no appreciable time would be allowed for the projectile to be accelerated up the barrel and the pressure behind it would burst the breech. This action is the very opposite of the classic explosion of the old time black powder shot guns where the action was a clear slow combustion of the fuel; they went off with a prolonged "wumph" instead of a "bang"!

Years ago, before the introduction of modern petrol and lubricating oils, motor car engines had to be decarbonised every few thousand miles. This irritating procedure was necessary because the combustion of the petrol and the burning of lubricating oils built up a deposit of carbon on top of the piston and on the inside of the cylinder head. This deposit reduced the volume above the piston and therefore increased the compression ratio of the engine to the point where it tended to run like a diesel engine igniting the fuel by the high compression. When this happened the ignition occurred too early in the piston's stroke and the increasing pressure caused the remainder of the fuel to detonate, producing a high pitched metallic rattling sound which was generally known as "pinking". Under these conditions the power output of the engine fell drastically, making going up hill a slow and difficult business.

A detonation in an airgun produces a very sharp rise in pressure within the cylinder which is often sufficient to cause the walls to bulge in front of the piston. The piston will then be smartly driven back against the spring at very high speed, often re-cocking the gun, or damaging the trigger mechanism. At the same time the pellet will usually leave the muzzle at high velocity accompanied by a very sharp crack - loud enough to make your ears ring - with plenty of smoke, and possibly an orange flame and sparks at the muzzle. However, although the pellet usually emerges at high velocity this does not always happen, many instances have been observed when the pellet has left the bore below the normal velocity for that rifle. In most instances the extremely fast return of the piston causes the gun to jerk violently, it also damages the spring causing its coils to be permanently forced closer together. This shortening of the spring reduces its energy storage capacity and therefore the future power of the rifle.

Some years ago an attempt was made to harness a detonation in the Weihrauch HW35/Barracuda. A small amount of an ether based substance was injected into the cylinder before each shot by a small pump fitted onto the cylinder. Like all detonations the results were unpredictable and the system was abandoned, history never mentions the damage that must have been caused to the spring by this fierce treatment.

A detonation has often been called a "diesel shot," or the gun has been said to be "dieselling." We realise that this is not quite true because, as we have already explained, a diesel engine relies upon high compression to fire the charge of fuel in a controlled and moderately gentle manner to drive the piston down. In a similar manner the propellant charge in a shotgun cartridge burns slowly enough to accelerate the shot up the barrel at the required rate. However, a "diesel shot" has all the characteristics of a detonation; the violence, the noise, the savage recoil and the sparks; so we now consider a "diesel" to be just another name for a detonation.

Although each of the four phases has been described on its own as a definite function, in fact it is quite possible for a rifle to slowly change and operate in each phase during a remarkably short span of time. Suppose the rifle were to be overhauled and far too much lubricant used, some of it allowed in front of the piston, then the first few shots might well be in the *detonation phase*, as shooting continued and the majority of the lube burned or splashed out into the stock, the gun would calm down and the shots would move into the *combustion phase*. If much more shooting was done and the original unsuitable lubricant became totally exhausted then the gun would revert right back to operating as a *popgun*. Further, if slack fitting pellets were later fired the rifle would certainly operate as a *blowpipe*. The whole sequence could then be reversed if, foolishly, a lubricant were to be injected directly into the transfer port.

The Nitrogen Experiment

Establishing the difference between the *popgun* and the *combustion* phase is not easy. Clearly there is a big difference between the velocity attainable by a well-oiled gun and one that is dry, the reason for this difference was originally thought to be the friction in the unlubricated condition. We tended to think that a dry leather piston head set up enough friction with the cylinder walls to kill all the power. We did many experiments, some of them quite bizarre, in the hope of isolating the energy produced by combustion from that provided by the spring; a gun was totally cleaned and washed out to remove all traces of oil or grease, then it was rebuilt using dry graphite powder as a lubricant - it sounded like a "bag of washers", but there was still the smell of exhaust. Even a totally dry gun was clearly finding something to burn because the acrid smell of exhaust at the muzzle was very obvious, even using pellets that had been thoroughly degreased still did not cure the smell.

Finally the "Nitrogen Experiment" was embarked upon. A .22 Weihrauch HW35 was stripped, degreased then carefully rebuilt employing the correct amount of lubrication everywhere. The gun was then fired continually over the chronograph until its velocity had settled to a constant figure of 636 FPS when shooting a 14.4 grain pellet. That is 12.9 Ft. lbs. We then placed the action of the gun together with a supply of pellets in a long plastic bag and sucked all the air out with a vacuum pump; we left it in the bag for about half an hour while the air, and especially the oxygen, was drawn out from the leather piston head and from any other crevices too.

The bag was then firmly sealed around the barrel and a rubber bung pressed into the muzzle to make it airtight so that no air could possibly re-enter it. Finally nitrogen, an inert gas that cannot support combustion, was blown into the bag expanding it to a manageable size for shooting, the gun was then loaded and fired a number of times, of course the bung in the muzzle had to be removed and refitted at each shot so that no oxygen could enter the system - loading the pellets was certainly no easy task. This time the gun only produced 426 FPS or 5.8 Ft.lbs.

Once the combustion had been eliminated by the nitrogen the gun's power had dropped dramatically and was only producing 45% of the original power - just under half - without interfering with the characteristics of the lubrication. The gun was later removed from the bag and fired in air as normal, the velocity soon returned to its original value. This little experiment proved to us once and for all that whatever lubrication is employed it will not only reduce the friction between the moving parts but will also add to the energy within the system by providing a combustible fuel.

All the facts and arguments regarding the four phases apply equally well to spring powered air pistols too. Although the spring power in a pistol is far lower than that in a rifle, the area of the piston is also reduced so the air pressure generated as the pistol fires is about the same, certainly it can be high enough to cause combustion.

Chapter 2 - The Four Phases

Chapter 3
THE SPRING

The definition of a spring is: " A device for storing energy." In the spring of a cocked air rifle the potential energy is said to be stored in the form of "Elastic" or "Strain" energy because it is accumulated by twisting the wire of the spring's individual coils, this can be clearly understood by looking at the illustration **fig 3.1**.

Imagine what happens as this spring is compressed; the wire in each coil is twisted until the coil lies flat on its neighbour, at the same time the energy used to twist it is stored within the wire. This potential energy will be converted into kinetic energy when the spring is released to drive the piston along the cylinder.

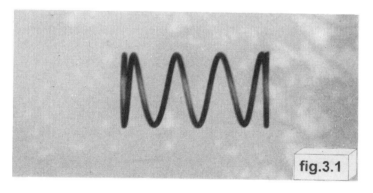

fig.3.1

There is however, obviously a limit to which the wire may be twisted before it becomes permanently deformed; imagine that the coils of the illustrated spring were spaced much further apart, then the wire would have to be twisted further before they became coilbound, probably causing a permanent deflection from which the wire would not recover; in other words the material has been "over stressed". Most air gun springs are designed to make the very best use of the material from which they are made and when fully compressed the stress in the wire is at the absolute maximum allowable, no improvement in performance can be made without the spring either breaking or becoming permanently deformed.

The spring maker must therefore ensure that the coils are not pitched too far apart even though it is tempting to make them wide in the interest of increased *Energy Storage Capacity (ESC)*. Each dimension of a spring influences the amount of energy it can store: the distance between the coils, the diameter of the wire, the diameter of the final spring and most of all the material from which it is made.

Airgun springs are made from wire which has already been hardened and tempered to the best possible degree, if it is too hard it will certainly break, while if it is too soft it will collapse the first time it is used. To coil the spring the wire is forced between three rollers which are set in a triangular formation and angled in such a way as to ensure that the wire is coiled to the desired pitch. It is an incredible sight to see the wire running around in the space between the rollers then spiralling out in front of them as an endless spring before being automatically cut off while the next unit is already on its way from the forming rollers. It is a continuous process in which the wire is fed from drums which can hold very large quantities of material. Each spring is wound with a pitch slightly greater than the wire can normally withstand, which of course means that the spring is also longer than we would expect when we buy it as a spare.

The end coils are closed down in the coiling machine before they are cut off from the next spring that is being wound; it is then passed through a stress relieving process consisting of heating for about half an hour to somewhere between three to four hundred degrees Celsius, this relieves the local stresses caused by the coiling. The springs then go into a special machine which grinds the ends flat so that they can lie perfectly square within the piston or, at the other end, fit correctly onto the spring guide.

Plenty of highly technical books have been written on the complex subject of springs, but none of them mention air gun springs. This is because our springs fall outside normal design parameters; by all reasonable standards they are grossly over stressed and only a few specialist firms are willing to manufacture them.

Most air gun springs are made from high quality wire to BS 5216 or BS 2803. This is the material that is most commonly used for springs throughout industry, but there are, of course, many other materials from which springs can be made: stainless steel for corrosive situations, or beryllium copper for non-magnetic applications. We are often asked if there is a better type of steel available which, although more costly, might provide a longer lasting spring that could also store more energy. As we understand it, there are such materials, but since they are not normally available the trouble and expense of making the special units is not worth the very doubtful advantage to be gained by their employment.

Springs made from square section wire instead of the conventional round material have recently appeared on the market. We carried out a comprehensive study of examples made from this material and found that if they are correctly made their performance is on a level with their round counterparts. However, we have seen examples where the wire has been cocked over obliquely to the centre line of the spring, in this formation the spring presents its sharp diagonally opposite corners to both the inside of the piston and the outside of the guide tube, from which they scrape metal as the piston moves. The continual scraping does irreparable damage as well as filling the gun with swarf.

It is possible to reduce the risk of spring breakage by a process known as shot peening. In this operation the spring is blasted all over by small steel shot of only 0.6mm diameter travelling at around 150 FPS. This has the effect of reducing the surface stress and thus the possibility of fracture through fatigue, a peened spring has a bright, frosted surface which feels slightly rough. A further stress relieving process must then carried out by heating it to between 200 and 250 degrees Celsius for about thirty minutes. It is arguable whether the slight extra cost involved in peening, relative to the spring's doubtful increased life span is worth while. It is a process which is far more valuable when applied to car valve springs which, although not as highly stressed as our springs, are certainly compressed and released many more times during their lifetime and need all the protection they can be given to avoid breakage.

It will be recalled that when the spring was first wound it was too long, this excess length is now corrected by to a process called "scragging." The spring is threaded over a rod and compressed down until it is coilbound. Upon release it should return only to the desired length, and it should stay at that length for the remainder of its useful life; unless of course it is subjected to the excessive forces generated by detonations, in which case it will have its length instantly reduced. The amount of extra length allowed at the coiling stage is a matter of experience depending mainly upon the characteristics of the material. If the spring maker does not get it correct then the final unit will not be the correct length and its ESC will be adversely effected.

The principle dimensions of a spring which influence its stiffness and therefore the amount of energy it can store, are as follows: if the diameter of the wire from which the spring is made is doubled then the spring will be sixteen times as stiff, that is of course if none of the other dimensions are altered. If the diameter of the spring itself is doubled then it will be only one eighth as stiff as previously. If the number of active coils is doubled in a spring of given length, then the stiffness is halved. Finally, of course, the material from which the spring is made is probably the most significant factor of all, influencing not only its strength but also its life. But of course the bottom line to all these statements is that the stiffer the spring the greater will be its ESC.

Calculating the spring power

Since so little energy is available in an airgun relative to a firearm it is very important to know just how much is available within the compressed spring, and also to know how efficiently it is employed in projecting the pellet when it is released. It is not too difficult to measure the amount of energy stored by a spring in a cocked gun, but it must be remembered that the energy figure (ESC) obtained only applies to that particular spring when fitted in a particular model, the same spring in another gun will have very different characteristics because dimensions such as the cocked and uncocked lengths have a profound effect on the amount of energy stored.

The amount of stored energy is best determined by the use of a graph which is constructed from the spring's own characteristics **fig 3.2**.

The most troublesome part of a spring's analysis is the determination of its length at two convenient loads, say 100 and 200 pounds. Once these two lengths have been found the rest is easy. It is the magnitude of the weights that produces the difficulty; this can only be solved by the researcher, but the method that is normally suggested is to stand the spring upright on the workbench then thread a long rod through the spring and through the bench, weights may then be attached to the lower end of the rod.

The first two points to be plotted on the graph are **A** & **B**. These are determined by subtracting from the free length the lengths of the spring when loaded with 100 lbs. and 200 lbs. The free length is of course the length of the spring when it is outside the gun, and the subtraction is necessary because the figures are deflections not lengths.

Spring Energy

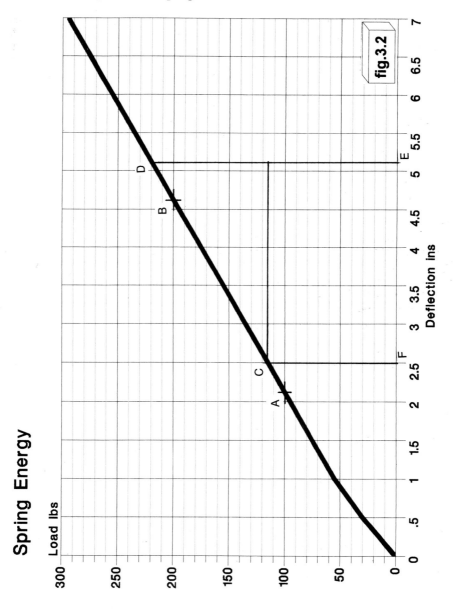

fig.3.2

Once the two points have been positioned a straight line may be drawn through them. Although in theory this straight line should pass through the zero point, in practice, however, it never does. This is due to a number of factors which do not concern us here.

Points **C** & **D** may now be positioned. Point **C** being the initial compression applied to the spring when fitted inside the uncocked gun; it is found by subtracting the uncocked length from the free length. Point **D** is the fully compressed length of the spring when the gun is cocked. It is found by adding the length of the piston's stroke to the initial compression point at **C**. Two vertical lines from the points **C** & **D** to the horizontal axis may now be drawn; the area contained within these lines represents the energy stored by the spring when the gun is cocked.

In the example we have taken to demonstrate this the dimensions were:

Free Length:	**10.0"**
Length at 100 lbs.load:	**7.9"**
Length at 200 lbs.load:	**5.4"**
Uncocked length:	**7.5"**
Piston Stroke:	**2.6"**

The calculation is:

Free length minus length at 100 lbs. gives point **A**. (10 - 7.9) = **2.1"**
Free length minus length at 200 lbs. gives point **B**. (10 - 5.4) = **4.6"**
Free length minus uncocked length (initial compression).
                    Point **C**. (10 - 7.5) = **2.5"**
Initial Compression plus piston stroke (total compression).
                    Point **D**. (2.5 + 2.6) = **5.1"**

These figures produce a diagram in the form of a trapezium whose area may be calculated to give a figure of 436.8 inch pounds: That is 2.6" x 116 lbs = 301.6 in. lbs. for the square section and $^{1}/_{2}$ (2.6 x (220 - 116)) to give 135.2 in lbs for the triangular section. So dividing 436.8 in lbs by twelve to convert to the more conventional figures we find that the spring stores **36.4 Foot Pounds.**

An interesting extension of this system, which eliminates the necessity of using two weights every time, is to carry out the above procedure on a spring which is then kept as a "master", the lengths at the two loadings being carefully kept with the spring. Future springs may then be threaded onto a piece of screwed rod end-to-end with the master; as soon as the master is compressed to the lengths which indicate the previous loads, it then follows that the compression of the unknown spring may be measured to obtain its deflection at the calibration loads.

Spring life

The working life of a spring has always been a constant source of difficulty, very often the spring is the first thing to be blamed when a sporting rifle's power deteriorates, yet in all probability the spring's performance is still more than adequate and what has actually happened is that the gun has burned up most of the original lubricant and is "out of fuel." All that is necessary to restore the power is to re-lubricate it.

On the other hand, the life of a spring in a lower powered competition target rifle is usually very long indeed because the gun is operating in the *popgun* phase and little or no lubricant is available to cause combustion, which in excess is so detrimental to the spring.

Taking as an example of spring damage, the case of a rifle whose owner has over lubricated it by injecting oil directly into the cylinder via the transfer port; after a few low powered shots during which most of the excess oil will be expelled, the quantity of lubricant present in front of the piston will reach a critical point and the gun will detonate. The enormous pressure will drive the piston backwards compressing the spring as hard as possible, perhaps even re-cocking the gun while at the same time a pronounced bulge may be formed in the cylinder.

Although it might be argued that it is impossible to compress a spring beyond the point where it is coilbound and therefore it can not be further strained even if a greater load is placed on it. This is not quite true, we have been advised by a leading spring manufacturer that in fact a spring can be subjected to excessive strain if the load is applied and released very fast indeed, allowing very energetic vibrations to be set up among the coils.

The exact sequence of events during which the spring becomes overstrained is not easy to follow and is best studied by calculation. Suffice to say that at very high speeds vibrations are set up within the coils which cause them to be stressed to a greater degree than when they are purely closed up tight. The problems with airgun springs arise from the very closeness of the coils when compressed and the very sudden release to its full length when fired. There would be no difficulty if they were released slowly, perhaps at the same speed as they are cocked; but just try to imagine what happens to the spring once the trigger is released. First of all the front coils thrust the piston forward with such speed that the tail end follows and is in fact dragged away from its seating against the trigger block; by this time the piston has been suddenly stopped on a cushion of air at the front of the cylinder and is now bouncing backwards down the cylinder to meet the forward moving tail coils of the spring, the condition will then immediately reverse, the piston and spring will try to drive each other in their original directions, a thoroughly chaotic state of affairs during which the spring will be overstrained and lose part of its length. The vibrations will be so severe that the piston and spring may be suspended for fractional moments within the cylinder without touching either end. They may both then complete a couple of smaller shuffles backwards and forwards along the cylinder before finally coming to rest, possibly even after the pellet has left the muzzle.

If there is excess oil present in the cylinder and the rifle detonates then the piston will be driven back very fast indeed against the forward moving tail coils of the spring, it is this very sudden and violent reversal of the spring's direction which causes the damage. The harm that the spring suffers by a detonation is usually very clearly shown by the coils becoming closed at the trigger end only; if a spring breaks, it is usually at this end that the fracture occurs. We were able to confirm this phenomenon some years ago by asking customers to return springs supplied by us for replacement if they failed in service. One end of the spring had previously been painted and the customer asked to fit it with the paint at the trigger end, it was always at this end that the trouble occurred.

In practical terms, over the years we have damaged many springs ourselves during experiments, in each instance the spring's length has been reduced by violent explosions inside the cylinder, on these occasions the pressure in front of the piston may rise as high as 20,000 PSI for an infinitesimally short interval of time. It may therefore be said that a detonation is death to a spring.

It has often been suggested that leaving a rifle cocked for long periods weakens the spring, this is probably true if the spring is not of top quality, but a properly made spring will withstand solid compression almost indefinitely without any loss of length. However as a safety precaution it is certainly advisable **never** to leave a rifle cocked for a minute longer than is absolutely necessary.

There is only one way in which a spring can lose its ESC, and that is by becoming shorter; they do not lose strength with age or by usage. Study of **fig.3.2** will show that if the spring we took as an example were to have its length reduced by a detonation and then re-tested, the height of the enclosed zone would be reduced and it would move to the left on the diagram thereby reducing its area, from which it follows that its ESC must also be diminished.

With this harmful reduction of a spring's length in mind, and the probability that a new spring is likely to be damaged by the combustion of excess lubrication immediately after an overhaul, it has been suggested that the old spring should be refitted during the overhaul. The new spring being inserted only after a number of shots have been fired and the rifle has settled down to give consistent velocity shots without excessive combustion. It is also a good plan to note down the length of a new spring before fitting it so that any loss of length may be checked at a future date.

Very often when a spring is removed it will be found to have bent rather like a banana; although this deformation is unsightly it will have no detrimental effect on the ESC of the unit, but will probably emphasise "spring twang" as the gun fires. Most of this irritating twang may be eliminated by the use of a thin plastic sleeve fitted around the spring as it is inserted into the piston, though a slight amount of clearance must be allowed inside the tube to accept the increase in the spring's diameter as the gun is cocked. Alternatively, spring twang may also be eliminated by a plastic guide running inside the spring in place of the steel guide. Most British manufacturers now fit plastic spring guides when they build their rifles and pistols because of the demand for quieter guns.

Since a spring's end rotates slightly as the gun is cocked, and rewinds itself to the same degree when it is fired, it has been suggested that it worthwhile making provision for this movement by some sort of antifriction bearing at one end in the hope of increasing the efficiency of the system. In our opinion this is a somewhat pointless exercise since, as we have already explained, there is a moment in the firing stroke during which the spring is either totally out of contact with its trigger end support, or only in very light contact with it. An interesting historical note here, to eliminate the problem of spring twist some early rifles were built with two short springs wound in opposite directions separated by a washer at the middle.

The optimum spring power required for a rifle depends on many factors, but at best it must be a compromise and the choice will depend on the purpose for which the rifle is intended. A low powered spring will have the advantages of low recoil and high consistency in velocity, because of these two factors good accuracy will result. On the other hand if the rifle is required for longer range shooting, perhaps for sport, then a greater energy input may be required and pinpoint accuracy sacrificed. However, that is not the end of the story, any airgun is a compromise between many opposing factors, only a few of which are embodied in the spring.

At the outset of our investigations we took, what we then thought to be the common sense view, that a rifle's performance depends totally on the power of the spring and nothing else. Since then we have grown to realise that the spring's performance is only one of many factors that go to make up the success of the gun, we have subsequently handled rifles which produced adequate powers without the necessity for huge springs. It is fair to say that if all the factors in a gun's performance are working together in a beneficial way the gun will not require a large energy input. The problem lies in understanding all the factors and persuading them to work together in the same direction.

Assuming one removes the spring from a rifle of unknown history, what should one look for as to its future value as a power unit. A visual inspection will soon reveal whether it has partially collapsed, indicated by the closeness of the coils at one section rather than another. This complaint is usually accompanied by buckling, which is easy to spot, since the spring will be visibly bent. Each of these ailments, (except buckling) reduce the performance of the unit by robbing it of its original length, which as we have already shown, is the important factor when evaluating a spring. Experience is the best judge in determining whether a spring which has been in service for some time has lost some of its original length. The following may serve as a rough guide; most springs, when new, have a gap of about one and a half times the wire diameter between the coils. But if the wire is thinner than normal the gap will increase to twice the wire diameter. Another indication is the amount of initial compression that has to be applied, in most instances this is about two inches. It is also advisable to check that the spring is almost coilbound when the gun is cocked, thus using the maximum energy available in that spring.

Whilst on the subject of unsuitable springs, the usual question must be answered: "Can a more powerful spring be fitted?" In most cases the answer is "No." Obviously if the original had lost length, or did not belong to the gun in the first place, then a new correct spring will be more powerful. A more powerful spring can only be longer or be made from thicker wire and so will probably not fit both inside the piston or over the spring guide. If it is longer, it will probably become coilbound before the gun can be cocked, so some coils will have to be removed.

Other types of spring

There are several rifles on the market that employ two pistons and therefore two springs, the pistons face each other from opposite ends of the cylinder and move together to drive the air upwards and outwards into the breech that lies approximately half way along the cylinder. However, the prime purpose of this system is to eliminate recoil rather than to increase the input energy.

Another system by which energy can be stored is by compressing air instead of compressing a spring **fig 3.3**. Gun makers Theoben use this system in their gas ram powered rifles; instead of compressing a spring as the rifle is cocked, air, or any other suitable gas, within a sealed cylinder is compressed. The cylinder in this instance being the piston itself which is forced backwards over a hollow dummy piston, the joint made perfectly airtight by a lip seal.

Referring to **fig 3.3**. The piston is shown half way along its stroke, as it moves backwards into the cocked position air is drawn into the cylinder **A** as in a normal spring rifle. At the same time air, or another gas is compressed into space **B** from inside piston **C**. The seal at **D** permanently prevents its escape from the system which was originally charged to its working pressure through a valve fitted inside the port at **E**. This initial charge should last indefinitely.

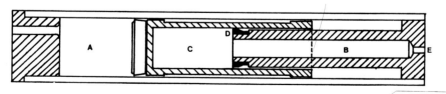

fig.3.3

Chapter 3 - The Spring

In all major respects the gun is conventional as regards cocking and loading, in fact unless one knows that the spring is missing together with the lack of noise and vibration, one is little the wiser. The same air is of course used over and over again, it does not have to be replenished after each shot. Although the term "gas ram" may sound unfamiliar, they are a very common device indeed, normally called a gas strut; modern cars use them to support the hatch back door, bonnet or boot lid when they are open. They appear as a long cylinder into which a highly polished rod is forced to compress the air as the boot is closed. The air, or in this case probably an inert gas such as nitrogen, is under terrific pressure at all times, but especially when the ram is closed, so they must *always* be treated with respect and never taken apart.

Theoben rifles derive many advantages from employing a gas ram instead of a coil spring; mainly because it never loses its power, and in some instances this power may be varied by adjusting the pressure inside the cylinder by means of a special air pump. There is no spring twang or vibration. Also, if any unsuitable lubricant or indeed if any lubricant at all, is injected into the cylinder, the resulting explosion will not have the same immediate damaging effect as it would were a conventional spring fitted. Inevitably though, prolonged misuse will reap its own rewards.

Chapter 4
THE CYLINDER

The cylinder of a spring rifle is not only the housing for the piston and its driving force, it is also the foundation for the whole construction. The trigger, the breech, the barrel, the sight, even the stock all use it as their attachment point, its strength and rigidity is therefore crucial to the success of the gun. The very fact that if the screws holding the stock to the cylinder are not fully tight the gun will not be accurate indicate the importance of the tube's rigidity. It is almost universally made from steel, the best known exception to this rule in spring guns is the Webley Eclipse. Webley took this revolutionary step in 1987 so as to reduce the weight of their new rifle to a point below that of their competitor's models; it looks as though they backed a winner because nearly ten years later the rifle is still in production. BSA have recently followed suite by using extruded aluminium for the cylinder and body of their 240 Magnum pistol.

Whatever the material used for the cylinder, its walls must be strong enough to resist enormous internal pressure if a detonation should occur. Such detonations can put a colossal strain on the material of the cylinder in front of the piston and we have seen several instances where the cylinder has become visibly bulged by such occurrences.

Besides being the physical foundation of the rifle, the cylinder is also the technical foundation. The early spring rifles that were popular in American shooting galleries all had very large diameter cylinders but their piston's stroke was relatively short. The guns were powered by two springs, each wound in the form of a cone from flat section spring steel and mounted inside the cylinder with the apex of the cones facing each other. Although the springs were very stiff, the output energy from these guns was low when compared with modern rifles, probably because the short stroke did not allow the piston to gain a high speed.

The modern trend is to have a smaller cylinder bore but allowing the piston a much longer stroke. Bore to stroke ratios have steadily climbed over the years and now stand at 1 to 3.7 in the case of the Webley Patriot ($1^3/_{16}$" x $4^3/_8$"). The greater the bore to stroke ratio the higher the efficiency of the whole system is likely to be, that is assuming that a spring of the correct matching power is fitted. There is inevitably a limit to the magnitude of the ratio. Quite obviously the smaller the diameter of the rifle's cylinder, the lower the power output is bound to be; unless of course the stroke is made disproportionately long. Also, the output power of such a rifle would of course not only be restricted by the reduced swept volume, but also by the difficulty of making a spring of high ESC which at the same time would fit inside the piston. Although such a rifle might not be powerful, its efficiency in terms of input/output energy would be high.

We did an elaborate experiment to gain information about the interaction of the three factors of bore diameter, piston stroke and spring energy. In any experiment one aims to vary only one factor at a time, in this case it was the piston's stroke; It was however, impossible to maintain the same input energy throughout the wide range of piston strokes, in spite of employing a number of springs and packing washers. Adjusting the stroke length of the 30mm diameter piston was not difficult, we cut its rod in half and joined it by a long stud onto which distance pieces were threaded **fig 4.1**.

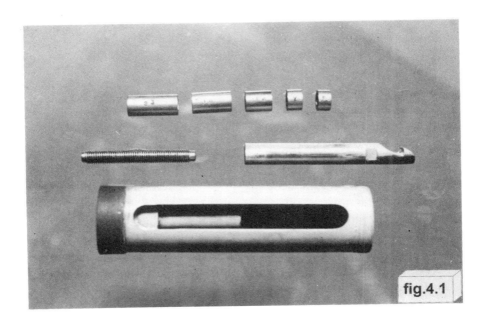

fig.4.1

During one part of this exercise we were able to maintain an energy input of 15 Ft.lbs. and using 12 Grain .22 pellets we found the following:

STROKE	RATIO	SWEPT VOLUME	OUTPUT	EFFICIENCY.
mm.	Bore : Stroke	cm³.	Ft.lbs.	Percent.
24	1:0.8	17.0	2.1	14.0%
30	1:1.0	21.2	3.1	20.6%
36	1:1.2	25.5	4.5	30.0%
42	1:1.4	29.7	4.8	32.0%
48	1:1.6	34.0	3.5	23.5%
54	1:1.8	38.2	3.4	22.6%
60	1:2.0	42.4	2.0	13.3%

The interesting point here is that when the bore to stroke ratio was 1:1.4, (42mm) the rifle, in this instance, gave its best output from a spring of 15 Ft. lbs. Either side of that 1:1.4 ratio the power started to decline. This demonstrates in a very clear manner that there is an optimum ratio for a given spring power for each size of rifle. Though it must be said that individual models of any make may vary in their optimum input power; this is probably due to a multiplicity of factors, many of them very small but together having a large effect on the characteristics of the rifle.

Further examination of *all* the figures obtained from this experiment, during which over a thousand shots were fired, show that larger bore to stroke ratios are always more efficient than small ones. Also, that in every case there was an optimum spring power for that ratio, increasing the input power beyond that point caused the output energy to fall.

Inevitably the presence of any combustible material in front of the piston will tend to magnify the efficiency figures, especially where the bore to stroke ratios together with the input energies are high. Efforts were made during the experiment to eliminate any extra energy entering the system through combustion, but this is next to impossible to achieve completely without recourse to an inert gas.

The dimensions of the cylinder control the compression ratio of the rifle, that is the amount by which the air is compressed when the rifle is fired. It is a slightly theoretical figure but one which gives a good guide to the probable efficiency figures to be expected. The "compression ratio", in air rifle terms, is the ratio of the air volume swept by the piston relative to the small volumes inside the transfer port and recesses in the piston head, even within the pellet itself. For example suppose the volume of the port and other small upswept volumes was one cubic centimetre while the volume swept by the piston was two hundred cubic centimetres, then the ratio would be two hundred to one.

More correctly, and particularly when speaking of motor engines, the compression ratio is the "total volume", that is the total volume in the cylinder when the piston is at the bottom of its stroke, divided by the "clearance volume" that is the total volume in front of the piston when it is at the top of its stroke. In our case we realise that there is so little clearance volume when the gun is uncocked that our definition makes the term clearer when speaking of airguns.

The compression ratio of spring guns has increased over the years because the length of the transfer port has decreased - the port has even been completely eliminated in some instances - with the result that the calculated ratio may exceed a thousand to one. We earlier said that this ratio is theoretical, this is because in most instances the pellet moves away up the bore before the piston reaches the end of its stroke and therefore the ratio falls from that moment and can never achieve its maximum value. Also, it must be remembered that at a certain point in its travel the piston will reverse its movement under the influence of the air it has compressed in front of its head.

Not many physical problems arise in an airgun through cylinder faults, but air leaks are not unknown. Most cylinders are made from tube with the front end held in place by screw threads, welding or brazing. Cases have arisen where air has leaked into the grooves cut into the end plug to carry the brazing material. This type of leak is extremely difficult to detect other than by pouring a small amount of oil into the cylinder then heating the breech so that air expanding through the flaw will produce a stream of bubbles. A thin film of solder over the whole area has always produced a satisfactory cure. A very few instances have been found where the stock mounting screw holes have been drilled too deeply and have penetrated the cylinder or transfer port.

Many of the holes and slots in the cylinder's walls have the sharp edges left on them by the original machining. In some instances the edges will have been made even sharper and more prominent by the cocking and firing of the gun, these obstructions must be removed with fine files before any attempt is made to slide a new piston into the cylinder, if they are not the edges and burrs will ruin the sealing edges of the piston head.

Chapter 4 - The Cylinder

Probably the most important aspect of the cylinder is the surface finish of its bore. The finish on the section of the cylinder wall that comes in contact with the piston's head is perhaps the most crucial area of the whole gun, certainly as far as performance is concerned. There are, in general terms two types of finish, rough and smooth. The choice depends on what the gun is to be used for. If it is to be a competition rifle in which consistency is of primary importance and velocity only secondary, then the bore will be highly polished so that the piston's head scrapes back any lubricant with it as the gun is cocked. This ensures that no oil can pass the head to be burned, adding to the gun's power, in other words it acts only in the *popgun* phase.

Alternatively, if the gun is to be used in the field, power will be of primary importance, then a roughened surface will trap oil in its grooves and furrows as the piston is drawn back. This oil will be picked up as the piston comes forward again and burned in the heat of compression putting the gun firmly into the *combustion* phase. This assumes of course that a modern plastic lip sealed piston head is fitted in both instances.

In the case of a leather head the situation is slightly different because leather tends to wipe any surface clean, either rough or smooth. Leather acts like a wick and absorbs the oil; squeezing it out again as it comes under compression. In this situation the finish on the cylinder walls is not so important, rough or smooth the leather will mop up the oil causing the velocity to be more erratic than if a plastic head were to be fitted.

Chapter 4 - The Cylinder

Chapter 5
THE PISTON

When one thinks about a piston one immediately visualises some sort of plug that slides inside a cylinder making an airtight seal with the walls. Certainly that would appear to be the dictionary definition, like everything else in airgunning there are the few inevitable "ifs" and "buts" to be added.

The piston in a modern spring rifle serves a number of ends, it is a mounting for the air sealing piston head, it contains and guides the spring and it provides a mass to carry kinetic energy when the spring is released.

Taking the last point first: we examined, in some detail, the effect of altering the weight of the piston by adding lead weights inside, by doing this it was possible to double its original weight. But the results surprised us, we had expected a large alteration in muzzle velocity, either up or down, we were not sure which. Instead there was a small reduction in velocity, but the gun immediately became very unpleasant to shoot because of a very pronounced jerk on firing.

We soon realised that within the limits imposed by its dimensions and the weights of practical materials, the mass of the piston cannot be varied greatly. To see the situation more clearly we usually apply a bit of imagination and suppose the piston to be very heavy indeed, then upon release it would be accelerated forward slowly causing more recoil than normal because as the spring pushes the weight forward it must also push the rifle backwards, not forgetting that the spring and its piston are a separate system within the body of the rifle, and not permanently attached to it. When the piston arrives at the other end of its stroke it will have gained considerable momentum and must impart a forward motion to the whole rifle as it violently compresses the air that remains within the cylinder. The result, even with a normal piston, is a profound whiplash effect which in its severest form may damage a telescopic sight or at least cause it to move backwards along the cylinder. A lightweight piston produces far less recoil but may be totally impractical to manufacture economically, and in any case the spring itself, which may be fairly heavy, is also responsible for some of the trouble and that can't easily be done away with. Whatever the weight of the piston the energy within the system is always the same, and that is the energy stored in the spring when the gun was cocked.

When the piston is heavy, the energy in the spring is transferred to it more slowly making the gun uncomfortable to shoot. However, a light piston can accelerate faster and hence less jerk is felt. When it arrives at the other end of the cylinder, a heavy piston is harder to stop than a light one, and although a cushion of air exists between the cylinder end and the piston head the effect of the piston's weight is still very clear.

A graph of typical piston travel against time is shown in **fig 5.1**. It can be seen that the velocity is approximately constant after the initial acceleration, until it nears the end of the cylinder, when it slows down abruptly and stops for an instant at about $\frac{1}{10}$ inch away from the cylinder end. From this position it bounces back to a point nearly $\frac{1}{2}$ inch away from the cylinder end, it then returns and comes to rest against the end of the cylinder.

Piston Travel

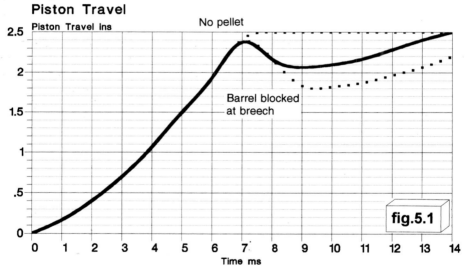

If there had been no pellet in the breech that piston would have carried on at the same velocity until it crashed into the end of the cylinder, doing no good to anything ! If, on the other hand, the barrel had been completely blocked and no air allowed to escape, then the piston would have bounced back much further than the $\frac{1}{2}$ inch. It would then have moved forward again and finally come to rest at the end of the cylinder.

Chapter 5 - The Piston

The reason that the piston is forced back, or bounces, is because at the instant when the piston is at the front of its stroke, the air is at its highest pressure; now the air is not able to transfer its energy instantaneously to the pellet since a pellet requires time to accelerate. Hence the highly compressed air forces the piston backwards until the forward thrust of the spring equals the backward thrust of the air. Of course, during this backward movement of the piston, the pellet has started off down the barrel, the piston again comes forward, this time completing its stroke.

If, however, it were possible to stop the piston from travelling backwards, this wasteful expansion of the air would be avoided and more energy would be imparted to the pellet. Having realised that this bounce caused such a great drop in cylinder pressure, we immediately set about trying to prevent it. We thought up many novel systems and wasted innumerable hours in attempts to hold the piston firmly in the forward position. It is comparatively easy to accomplish this on a slow speed trial when the piston is moved back and forward under hand control, but as soon as the gun is fired problems arise. First of all, the piston is at the front of its stroke for an infinitesimal instant of time and secondly, the pressure being exerted on it at that moment is enormous. Any device capable of restraining it must be able to act instantaneously and must also be strong enough to withstand the backward thrust of the piston, which is the maximum cylinder pressure multiplied by the frontal area of the piston. In our case this resulted in a force of over 1,000 lbs. Almost half a ton!!

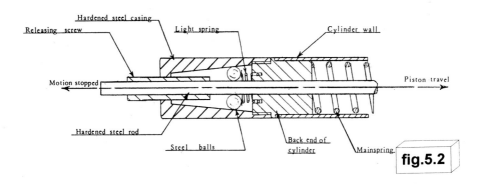

fig.5.2

A sketch of our final attempt is shown in **fig 5.2.** The idea is that the rod can pass freely in the direction of forward piston travel, but as soon as it attempts to return, the steel balls lock inside the tapered casing and prevent any further movement. When reloading the rifle, the balls are held away from the casing by the release screw which must be operated at each shot. All the parts of this device were made from tool steel then hardened and polished. Yet, in spite of all our endeavours, upon firing, all the working parts were distorted and the whole unit dragged away from the rear of the gun. At this point we decided that the scheme was impractical because it had become abundantly clear that the forces involved were greater than the normal gun could stand. If a gun could be built that incorporates a non return device, we foresee that the increase in velocity would be significant. It is a great pity that this must remain a debatable point that we have not been able to settle by practical experiment.

Theoben partially overcome the adverse effects of piston bounce by fitting an inertia piston inside the main piston of their gas ram rifles (**fig 3.3**). This cunning device is similar in shape to a cotton reel, but the hole through the centre is much smaller and the reel is fitted with 'O' rings instead of flanges. These rings ensure that under normal circumstances the inner piston stays put, such as when the rifle is being carried or pointed up or down.

When the rifle is cocked the inertia piston is pushed to the front end of the piston and is held there by the 'O' rings. Immediately the piston is released and starts moving forwards the inertia piston, being fairly heavy, tries to stay in its original position relative to the outside of the gun, allowing the main piston to move over it. But, by the time the main piston has reached the front of its stroke the inertia piston has changed its mind and is moving forward too, just in time to meet the main piston coming back as it bounces off a cushion of compressed air at its front. This sudden extra thump administered to the main piston by the inertia piston has many benefits, it increases the overall efficiency by reducing the piston bounce; also the main piston can be lighter than normal which reduces recoil or more correctly the jerk of the rifle.

There is another important factor in this system, the small hole drilled through the centre of the inertia piston allows air to pass in a controlled manner from one side to another. The size of this hole is crucial to the correct working of a system which, although appears simple, is in fact mind blowing in its complexity, requiring thought in at least four dimensions, inertia, speed, friction and airflow. If one factor is incorrectly gauged, then instead of improving the performance, the gun will become very rough indeed.

Chapter 5 - The Piston

There are two basic designs of piston, one has a rod running down its entire length terminating in a notch, or more correctly in gunmaking terms, a "bent", with which the sear engages as the gun is cocked; the alternative piston has no central rod, the bent being cut directly into the end of the skirt. There is no technical advantage in either system, the choice being a matter for the designer when he lays out the rifle and decides on the style and position of the trigger mechanism.

The skirt of the piston is pressed very firmly against the top of the cylinder by the end of the cocking link as the piston is pulled into the cocked position; this movement under pressure very often scores the skirt as well as the top of the cylinder bore, especially if the lubrication has been neglected. The problems associated with rubbing a steel piston against a steel cylinder may be eliminated if a nylon or soft metal liner, such as brass, is fitted to the piston's end, though this solution is usually left to the owner rather than employed by the manufacturer.

A piston must move with incredible speed when the rifle is fired and therefore friction or any other factor that tends to impede its progress must be suppressed or, if possible, eliminated. Grease or oil between two close, fast moving surfaces will tend to slow them down through "drag" and of course the heavier the lubricant in terms of viscosity the greater the drag will be. This drag may be reduced by decreasing the area of the surfaces in immediate contact with each other; it is for this reason that the central portion of the piston's skirt should always be machined to a smaller diameter than the two ends that guide it along the cylinder's bore. The reduced body diameter not only cuts down the area of the surface in contact with the cylinder but also provides a reservoir area for grease which will slowly move forward along the piston each time the gun is fired.

The slow forward motion imparted to the grease is caused by the piston's bounce, as the piston rushes forward it carries a film of grease with it which continues forward as the piston bounces back. But at the next shot the grease will tend to move backwards slightly as the piston starts its forward stroke; so it is a case of "One step back and two forward" at each shot. Eventually the grease will end up as a thick collar wedged firmly behind the piston head from where it will slowly move forward to the front if the rifle is intended for use in the *combustion* phase.

Some gun makers machine a slot right through the side of their pistons along which the cocking link slides, in some instances bumping over the coils of the spring as it goes. Other makers insert a shim steel case around the spring, partly to keep the cocking link from dragging on the spring and partly perhaps to reduce the amount of grease that can move from the spring into the cylinder. Again, some makers only machine a flat or shallow groove along which the link can slide, there being no communication between the inside of the piston. A prime example of this being the Theoben, where the inside of the cylinder contains air under pressure.

The reason for discussing the slot in the piston's side is to emphasise that very often the spring is also the storage reservoir for lubricant, or fuel, when this is the case it must have an easy but controlled access to the cylinder. Of course if the gun is designed to be used in the *popgun* phase then the less lubricant that finds its way to the front of the piston the better, in this instance it is preferable to eliminate the slot altogether.

Chapter 6
THE PISTON HEAD

We have devoted a whole chapter to the piston head, this is because all our experiments have shown that although it is small, it is probably the most important component of any spring gun having a greater influence on the performance of the system than most owners imagine. The head not only controls the phase in which the rifle operates, but also the shot to shot consistency. In the past what we now call the head was always known as the piston washer; that was not an unreasonable name when it was a simple disc cut from leather. As time went on the disc became a leather cup with a disc of leather filling up the space inside the cup; these days it is a very sophisticated component usually moulded from polyurethane.

When we first started to investigate how spring guns worked, we had assumed that a piston head should provide a frictionless yet airtight seal between the piston and the cylinder walls. We went to enormous lengths to achieve what we considered to be a perfect piston head, that is one which did not allow any air to pass it, yet at the same time was virtually frictionless when sliding down the bore. Probably the ultimate in a long line of experimental units is the one shown in **fig 6.1.** It is made up from four plastic rings each of which can expand or contract with minimum effort so as to form a perfect seal with the cylinder wall.

fig.6.1

The Air Gun from Trigger to Target 45

We gauged the quality of the seal between the piston head and the cylinder wall by firing the rifle when the barrel was blocked at the breech, the time taken between releasing the piston and it finally coming to rest gave a figure for the efficiency of the seal; this came to be known as "the piston time." Blocking the breech safely and without damage to the rifling was a problem in the early days, until we hit on the idea of using a device which, because of its similarity to an early Russian satellite, we called "The Sputnik". It is shown in **fig 6.2.**, in simple terms it is a cap which may be clamped onto the rifle's muzzle by the three screws, it firmly grips a thin rod running down the bore as far as the breech where it supports a pellet whose skirt is sealed by a small amount of Plasticine behind it.

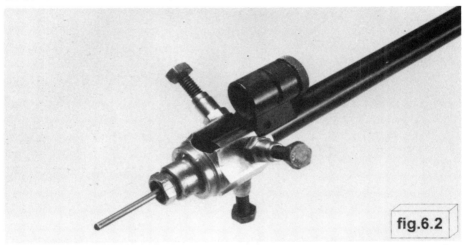

fig.6.2

We soon realised that a rifle fitted with what we considered to be a perfect piston head, that is one which gave an almost infinite piston time, never produced the power that we expected. A leather head, on the other hand, which gave us an approximate time of only four seconds was far more satisfactory. Also, we learned that a tight piston head, for whatever cause, was a guarantee of low power.

About this time a fellow enthusiast sent us a home made solid nylon head that carried the classic scars made by very hot gasses passing through a narrow gap at high pressure (**fig 6.3**). This head gave us the clue that perhaps we were dealing with something far more complicated than we had ever imagined.

Chapter 6 - The Piston Head

Further experiments with Perspex viewing windows fitted at the front of the cylinder and in the transfer port showed that when the rifle was working well and producing its maximum power there was a bright flash of white light occurring at the front of the piston, also that the main combustion was in fact occurring not so much in the cylinder itself but in the transfer port.

fig.6.3

Leather heads are very forgiving when it comes to rough treatment, on occasion we have seen ball bearings, tacks, nails and matches embedded in leather heads; yet after picking out the "foreign bodies" the heads were still serviceable (**fig 6.4**). This type of head will also survive long periods of use without lubrication and still return to life after a good soaking in oil.

fig.6.4

Chapter 6 - The Piston Head

Heads in the form of leather cups were the obvious solution to sealing the air inside the cylinder in various forms. They became the standard seals fitted to airguns in the past; though Webley favoured metal piston rings in their early rifles and pistols; while BSA later used synthetic rubber 'O' rings in theirs. Hindsight would indicate that in the case of rings the seal was probably too good and little or no lubricant could pass to the front of the piston to provide the fuel for combustion, resulting in a gun which could only operate under conditions of restricted combustion.

Airguns, both rifles and pistols, designed specifically for paper target competitions, benefit from a head fitted with ring seals because virtually no lubricant can pass them and the resulting highly consistent, yet low velocity shots without any combustion are exactly what are required in that sport.

Leather cup heads (**fig 6.5**) have some curious characteristics though, some heads would give exceptional powers simultaneously with very good consistency; yet another head would be hopeless, low power together with a wide spread of velocities. The reason behind these variations is not altogether clear; perhaps the success of the head depends of the position on the hide from which it was cut, or the tanning treatment to which the hide was subjected before the washer was cut. The processes through which a hide is passed between being a cover for the animal and a head for a piston are diverse, long and complicated and therefore allow plenty of scope for variations in the properties of the final product.

fig.6.5

Since leather has characteristics rather like a sponge, it has the property of absorbing oil. This absorbtion is naturally slow, and when the leather is formed into a piston head the rate of absorbtion is further influenced by whether the head was manufactured with what we call the shiny side, on the inside or outside. Leather has two sides, the shiny side and the rough side. The shiny side is the outside of the hide which carried the hair when it was on the animal, at the same time forming a semi waterproof barrier against the rain, it therefore absorbs oil very slowly. Alternatively the rough side is the side which used to be on the inside and can absorb water or oil much faster.

Most commercial leather heads are moulded with the shiny side outside and therefore restrict the speed at which the oil will be absorbed from the piston and cylinder, this leads to the odd phenomenon that spring guns usually produce higher velocities than normal immediately after standing for some time - especially with the muzzle pointing down. Excess oil will have been absorbed by the leather while the gun was not in use; it will then be burned up fast on the first few shots to give high velocities before being replaced at a slower rate at each subsequent shot. The reverse of this situation has also been observed, where the rifle has been standing on its butt for long periods, the combustible fractions of the oil will have drained away from the piston head leaving it dry and therefore unable to produce high velocities. This leads to the obvious statement that spring guns should be stored horizontally, preferably with the trigger uppermost - an odd posture for any gun.

We did a series of experiments with different types of head to investigate the effect of removing the shiny side from the leather. Using a standard plastic head as a reference base, velocities of about 670 FPS were recorded with 8.3 grain .177 pellets. The standard leather head with its shiny side outside started off - after being soaked in lubricant -with high velocities around 800 FPS, but these gradually fell to around 600 FPS indicating that it could not "wick" enough fuel through the leather to sustain maximum power. The final head had its shiny surface ground away to improve its wicking and absorbtion abilities; its performance rose gradually over about twenty shots to give a consistent velocity of 750 FPS. Throughout these tests a fairly "active" lubricant was used so as to emphasise the effect of the wicking action. (**fig 6.6**).

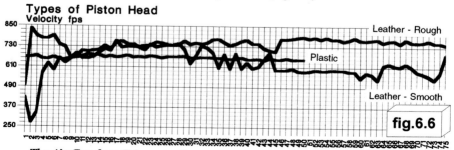

Types of Piston Head

The Air Gun from Trigger to Target

Of course no oil can possibly pass through a plastic head, so it has to rely on another totally different system to supply fuel for combustion. These heads, which are usually made from a grade of polyurethane, are designed with a lip at the front which faces ahead to scrape the oil along as the piston moves to the front of the cylinder. In the last chapter we described how lubricants build up like a collar just behind the piston's head and how this collar is held there because as the piston bounces, the lubricant that is clinging to it is moved forward towards the head at each shot. This collar provides the reservoir of oil which replenishes that moved forward by the lip at each cycle.

The amount of fuel passed forward at each stroke can be controlled fairly accurately by the "fit" of the head in the bore. Normally the sealing lip at the front is very flexible and exerts little pressure on the walls ensuring adequate lubricant remains to be moved forward. It is the body of the head behind the lip, which controls the size of the collar of lubricant and therefore the amount available to pass forward. We found that by reducing the diameter of this part of the head by grinding we could control the rate of combustion. The polyurethane plastic normally used for moulding these heads is very soft and difficult to cut accurately by any means other than grinding, or at least by rotating fast against a pad of glasspaper.

Normal systems of measurement such as verniers or micrometers are very unreliable when dealing with soft plastic; so we gauged the fit of the piston inside its cylinder by measuring the force necessary to move the piston down the lubricated bore, see **fig 6.7**. We found that when the cylinder was mounted upright in a vice, a weight of six pounds was necessary to move a new head down the bore; at this figure the gun operated slightly above the pop gun power. In other words it was not being supplied with much fuel. Adjusting the size of the head until half a pound would just move it, proved to be too slack and the gun immediately became unstable giving very erratic, mostly high, velocities. Further experiments with the size of the head showed that approximately two pounds thrust gave maximum power without instability.

A leather head wipes most of the lubricant from the polished cylinder walls as it is drawn back on the cocking stroke, some of it being absorbed by the leather to replace that which was burned at the previous shot, the remainder collects behind the head to form a collar of grease and oil which is smeared onto the walls as the gun fires. The cycle is then repeated each time the rifle is fired. The piston rushes forward, lubricating the cylinder as it goes, and a small amount of oil is burned as it reaches the end of the cylinder. In most rifles, the spring after firing holds the head against the cylinder end, keeping the leather firmly compressed so that it is unable to soak up much of the free lubricant to replace that which was burned, until the next cocking stroke. This power reducing characteristic may be eliminated by fitting a resilient plug inside the cup so that the leather is not under compression when the gun is uncocked.

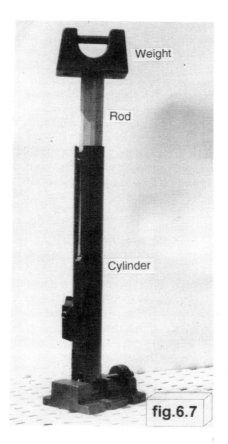

fig.6.7

The sequence with a plastic head is that when the piston is drawn back to cock the gun, the lubricant behind the head is spread thinly onto the cylinder walls by the lips of the seal and rubbed into the grooves and hollows left by the honing stones as they were rotated in the bore during manufacture. When the piston comes forward on the firing stroke, the lip at the front of the head scrapes the lubricant from the walls and carries it forward to the end of the cylinder, where it will be burned as the pressure and temperature rise. Although the whole system sounds a bit "iffy", in practice it can work very well and consistently for long periods, in fact right up to the point where it runs out of fuel. No engineer in his right mind would suggest making a diesel engine whose fuel was supplied in a similar manner, yet as far as we are concerned the fast forward and return or -*bounce*- of the piston provides just the right movement to keep the gun supplied with the correct amount of fuel for each shot.

The secret of the success of a plastic head lies in the roughness of the cylinder walls against which it rubs; it needs a slightly coarse surface which can store the lubricant in its microscopic troughs and hollows. A plastic head fitted in a cylinder whose walls have been highly polished will give good consistency but not the maximum power of which the gun is capable; this is because there is not enough fuel available to generate good combustion. A leather head on the other hand works best with smooth walls. This is because less friction is generated by the sides of the cup as they are expanded against the cylinder bore by the enormous pressure generated inside them, especially at the end of the stroke.

It is highly probable that because the piston comes forward so fast, the lubricant will be atomised by the lip of the plastic seal as it is stripped from the walls to form a fine mist. An atomised spray will of course burn faster and more efficiently than a film which has been peeled off the walls to form a solid mass on the front of the piston. The same argument might be applied to a rifle fitted with a leather head; in this instance however, the lubricant will be stored in the leather like water in a sponge, but when the sponge comes under sudden compression its charge of lubricant may again be squeezed out in the form of a mist. Realistically, this is only a theory which has yet to be proved by practical experiment.

It is interesting to notice that when a rifle has been overhauled and the remains of the old lubricant cleaned out, also, perhaps a new spring fitted and re-lubricated; the first couple of shots will be of low velocity. These may be followed by a few at very high velocity before the gun settles down to its consistent power. This initial wide variation in velocity can be explained by the lubricant moving slowly forward from the spring and body of the piston before it forms into the important 'collar' of fuel behind the head from where it can be distributed evenly at each shot. The few shots at extra high velocity are probably due to the small amounts of fuel that have slowly built up at the front of the piston becoming large enough to burn energetically, or even detonate. However, it must be admitted that the exact reason for these shots is still obscure and the explanation for their presence may provide a clue to a deeper understanding of spring guns.

Not all manufacturers make use of the roughened surface of the cylinder walls to capitalise on its benefits, even though they use a plastic lip sealed head, instead the bore of the cylinder is left with the degree of finish provided by the tube manufacturer. The tube is then chemically blacked with the rest of the gun's components. However, it has been our experience over the years that the blacking on a metal surface increases its coefficient of friction many times, so the piston's movement may well be impeded by its presence in the bore.

The amount of fuel available at the front of a leather head may be controlled by increasing the surface area exposed to the high pressure air; most leather heads have a plastic or metal disc in their centre through which a screw passes to hold them firmly onto the piston, if leather is substituted for this plastic and the shiny surface removed from the outside of the head so as to increase the absorbtion rate, then in all probability the gun will become unstable through the availability of excessive fuel. The actual amount of fuel burned at each shot, whatever type of head is fitted, must be very small indeed, perhaps about one tenth of the weight of a postage stamp.

The piston time test will immediately show up a fault in an old plastic head, such as a split at the bottom of the lip groove. Occasionally these heads may leak because a small piece has been shaved from the lip as the piston was inserted past the screw threads or cocking slot, this will reduce the piston time to the point where investigation is advisable. A replacement head should immediately cause the time to rise to a matter of hours rather than seconds. Alternatively a leather head usually has a shorter piston time than its plastic counterpart, but if the time becomes excessive the fit of the head should be checked because it indicates that the head has become compacted to the point where it is creating friction and its wicking ability is also being impaired, thereby starving the gun of fuel.

When stripping a gun for an overhaul, or just for an inspection of its condition, it is well worth taking the trouble of withdrawing the piston slowly and carefully so as not to disturb the grease that is still clinging to it. Examination of the grease behind the head can reveal plenty about the condition of the lubricant also about its suitability. At the same time the front of the head can tell the observant owner much about the gun's condition, for instance if the front of the head is covered by a layer of grease it will indicate that the pressure attained on compression is not high enough to burn it, or perhaps that the piston is allowing too much lubricant to pass forward at each cycle. A light brown coloured front face on a plastic head usually indicates that all is well and the fuel is being burned efficiently, that is if the gun is working in the *combustion* phase. Alternatively if the gun is being used for competitions and is adjusted to work in the pop-gun phase than the front of the piston should be dry and of the natural colour of the plastic from which it was made. It is difficult to tell anything from the colour of a leather head, they all look the same; but its wetness or perhaps dryness is a good indicator of its condition and the suitability of the lubricant being used.

It is debatable whether a leather or plastic piston head expands with enough force under the pressure of combustion to cause it to grip the cylinder walls firmly and thus resist its backward travel. This situation would certainly improve the efficiency of the whole system by reducing piston bounce and increasing the pressure behind the pellet.

Theoben Engineering have taken the concept of the plastic piston head a stage further with their Zephyr head. Its outline follows the normal design of a plastic head, but it has a number of shallow grooves cut into its front face radiating out from a shallow depression which matches the entry to the transfer port. As the piston completes its stroke, the air remaining in the cylinder is guided to the port increasing the efficiency of the system **fig 6.8**.

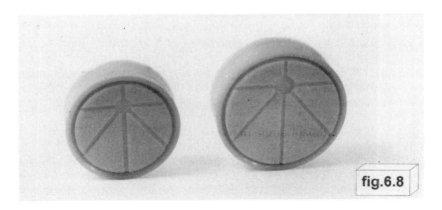

fig.6.8

Chapter 7
THE AIR

We all know what is meant by "An airgun," and we also know that the name covers a number of very different systems, the two main divisions are of course the "spring gun" and the "pneumatic."

In each of the two systems the air is used in a very different way; in the first it acts purely as a medium coupling the heavy slow-moving piston to the light fast-moving pellet. It adds no energy to the system, unless of course it supports combustion of the lubricant. In a pneumatic the air takes the place of the spring, storing energy until it is transferred to the pellet when the trigger is released.

This chapter will only be concerned with the air in a spring gun. We will describe, first of all, how the air behaves when no combustion takes place, which is the *popgun* phase. Later we will look at it when its oxygen component combines under heat and pressure with the combustible fractions of the lubricant to constitute the *combustion* phase.

The air rifle was preceded in history by the bow and arrow, and it is interesting to compare the two systems because they are both similar in that the projectile is accelerated by a spring, the wooden bow being the counterpart of the coiled steel in the rifle. There is however, one great difference between the two; in the bow no air is employed, whilst in the rifle, air is interposed between the spring and the projectile. The air is necessary because of the great disparity between the mass of the tiny pellet and that of the heavy spring and piston; whereas in the bow and arrow, the mass of the projectile is approximately equal to that of the bow string and the lighter sections of the bow that bend to fire the arrow. The air in the gun may be compared with the gearbox in a motor car, linking or 'matching' the slow-moving wheels and body to the light, fast-moving engine.

It is very important to thoroughly understand the function of the air in a rifle, so let us take it to the extreme and imagine how we might get along without any at all. Just suppose that we were to saw the barrel off a rifle, then place a pellet directly on the top of the piston; on firing the gun the pellet would fly away with the same maximum velocity as the piston had attained as it moved forward up the cylinder, about 50 FPS. Obviously this is very low when

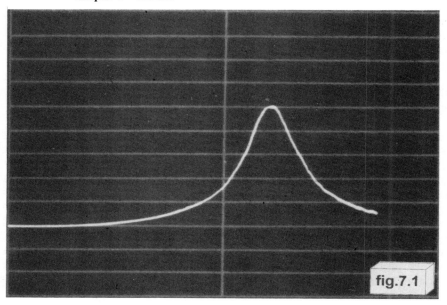

fig.7.1

Adiabatic Compression

(In a 1 inch diameter cylinder)

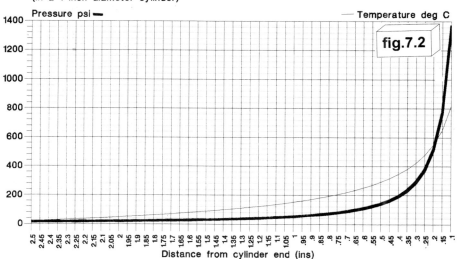

fig.7.2

The Air Gun from Trigger to Target

compared with the probable muzzle velocity the pellet would have attained from a complete rifle. The pellet's energy at this velocity would also have been correspondingly low since the pellet is so light.

Applying the same reasoning, if we were to load the same sawn off rifle with a lead ball whose weight approximately equalled the weight of the piston, then the ball would emerge with about the same velocity as before, (50 FPS) but being heavier, its muzzle energy would be far higher since the energy is proportional to its mass. This extra energy shows that by using the heavier ball we have achieved a far better "match" between the projector and projectile.

Now that we have determined the reason why air is necessary, what are the pressures involved inside the airgun cylinder ? This difficult parameter can only be measured satisfactorily by the use of a 'piezo ceramic transducer' and its associated charge amplifier. These instruments can be made into very small robust units which can be screwed directly into gun barrels or air rifle cylinders, they therefore lend themselves admirably to the study of internal ballistics. The pressure transducer converts pressure into an electrical charge that is processed by the charge amplifier. The resulting signal may then be displayed on an oscilloscope see **fig 7.1.**

In our case, the oscilloscope trace takes the form of a curve in which the vertical axis represents pressure and the horizontal represents time (not piston travel). As explained in chapter 5, the piston travel can be related to time, so this creates no problems when drawing a pressure/volume curve. The curve shown in **fig 7.2.** is similar only this time it has been based on the theoretical calculated figures and continues on upwards long past the point where the pellet would normally release and allow the pressure to fall again.

From these curves we are able to establish that for all practical purposes, the compression is *adiabatic* and that the peak pressure inside a typical cylinder is in the order of 1250 PSI. Adiabatic means that the compression takes place without any 'loss or gain of heat into or out of the system'. It must be understood that it is a basic law of physics that whenever a gas is compressed its temperature rises. If the rate of compression is high enough to prevent any heat escaping through the pump walls, the compression is said to be adiabatic. If, on the other hand the pumping is slow enough to allow the heat to escape, the compression is said to be *isothermic.*

Pumping up a bicycle tyre is a good example of isothermic compression because the slow steady strokes allow the heat in the compressed air to escape to the atmosphere through the pump body and connecting tube. Alternatively a spring airgun must be the classic example of an adiabatic compression, since the action is very fast.

Calculating the Pressure

Now that we have established that the compression is adiabatic, we can calculate the theoretical pressure and temperature from the following equations:-

$$P_1 . V_1{}^n = P_2 . V_2{}^n \quad \ldots \ldots .(1)$$

Which gives us the initial relationship between the absolute temperature and the volume.

P_1 = Initial pressure.
V_1 = Initial volume.
P_2 = Final pressure.
V_2 = Final volume.
n = Ratio of the specific heat capacities of the gas.
(Which for air has the value of 1.408)

$$T_1 . V_1{}^{n-1} = T_2 . V_2{}^{n-1} \quad \ldots \ldots .(2)$$

Which gives us the relationship between the absolute temperature and the volume.

Where:
T_1 = Initial temperature of the gas in Kelvin.
(i.e.) Degrees Centigrade + 273
T_2 = Final temperature of the gas in Kelvin.

Also the work done on, or by, the air when the volume changes from V_1 to V_2 is given by the equation:

$$\text{Work done} = \frac{P_2 . V_2 - P_1 . V_1}{n - 1} \quad \ldots \ldots .(3)$$

Before applying any of these equations to our problems, we must first fully understand how the air is actually compressed within the airgun cylinder. This may at first seem to be obvious, but it is in fact not quite as simple as one imagines.

When the trigger is pulled, the piston is released and is forced forward by the compressed mainspring. From the moment of release it is pushing the air inside the cylinder into a smaller and smaller space, thus causing an increase in pressure. But at a certain point the piston cannot compress the air any further and is forced backwards by it for some little distance before coming forward again, in other words the piston bounces.

In order to understand this more fully, consider a bicycle pump that has been blocked off and made airtight. If it is now supported vertically, the handle drawn up and a weight attached, it will be noticed on releasing the weight, the piston falls then bounces back off the cushion of air that it has compressed.

The exact same procedure takes place in the airgun cylinder, only much faster, the whole cycle lasting only about 15 milliseconds. (That is the time taken for a pellet travelling at 500 FPS to cover a distance of 7.5 Ft.!).

We have seen in Chapter One that at the point at which the piston starts its backward bounce the pellet releases and accelerates up the barrel. Or looking at it another way, the pellet holds back the air until a maximum pressure is reached, at which point the grip of the pellet is overcome and it starts away. At the same moment the piston can deliver no further thrust to the air because of its slow speed and therefore lack of energy. From this moment it is pushed backwards by the air in front of it. These are the events taking place when the pellet is the correct fit in a breech of optimum shape (see Chapter Nine). Without these important factors, the piston travel and pellet start times are upset, resulting in lower efficiency.

The graph of piston travel against time (**fig 5.1.**) shows the acceleration of the piston from the moment the trigger is pulled to the time that the piston hits the end of the cylinder, having bounced once on the cushion of air that it has compressed.

It is clear from this graph that the point of smallest volume corresponds, in our example, with a piston position of 0.10 inches away from the cylinder end. Since this is the point of smallest volume, it must also be the point of greatest pressure. We may now proceed to calculate the value reached at the peak pressure. Let us call the volume at this point V_2.

Applying equation (1):

$$P_1 . V_1{}^n = P_2 . V_2{}^n$$

P_1 will equal normal atmospheric pressure, since at this point the piston has not yet started to compress the air.

V_1 is the initial volume of the air in the cylinder, that is the volume before the piston starts to move.

Since in this case the cylinder diameter was 1 inch and the piston stroke 2.5 inches we can calculate the volume:

$$V_1 = \pi r^2 h = 3.142 \times 0.5^2 \times 2.5$$
$$= 1.964 \text{ cu. ins.}$$

$$P_1 = 14.7 \text{ psi}$$

$$V_2 = \pi r^2 h = 3.142 \times 0.5^2 \times 0.1$$
$$= 0.0785 \text{ cu. ins.}$$

$$\& \quad P_2 = P_1 \left(\frac{V_1}{V_2} \right)^n$$

Thus: <u>$P_2 = $ **1366 psi.**</u>

Since the above calculations cover a typical rather than a particular case, the lost volume of the transfer port has not been taken into account. This is because, during our experiments, the size and shape of the transfer port were altered. But it would be a simple matter to establish the volume of the port and add the figure to V_1 and V_2 at the start of the calculation.

This value of P_2 is therefore, the maximum pressure reached inside the cylinder. It must, however, be emphasised that this pressure is only reached for an instant and the slightest backward movement of the piston causes it to drop dramatically. If one looks at the adiabatic curve drawn in **fig 7.2**. one will realise that a backward movement of only 0.02 ins. will drop the pressure from 1350 to 1000 PSI !! And a further drop to about 500 PSI is brought about if the piston moves back only 0.1 inch.

Calculating the Temperature

When the piston accelerates forward, the Kinetic Energy that it contains is not only used in compressing the air but also, unfortunately, in heating it up. Thus, the temperature increases tremendously with the exponential rise in pressure. The new temperature can be calculated from equation (2).

$$T_1. \, V_1^{n-1} = T_2. \, V_2^{n-1}$$

$$T_1 = \text{Room Temperature} = 20 \, ^0C$$
$$= 20 + 273 \, K$$

$$V_1 = 1.964 \text{ cu. ins. (as before)}$$

$$V_2 = 0{,}0785 \text{ cu. ins. (as before)}$$

$$\& \quad T_2 = T_1 \left(\frac{V_1}{V_2} \right)^{n-1}$$

Thus:
$$\underline{T_2 = 1098 \, K \, = \mathbf{816 \, ^0C}}$$

At this temperature it is easy to see why oil, or anything else combustible in the cylinder ignites, and the gun is said to be "dieselling."

Once again we must emphasise that this temperature, like the pressure, is only reached for a fraction of a second. The rise in temperature can be seen against piston travel in **fig 7.2.**

It was said in our definition of an adiabatic compression, that no heat enters or leaves the gas, as in the case of a spring airgun. Although the temperature of the air has risen, the rise is solely due to the increase in internal energy, and not to any transference of heat, there is just not time for a significant transfer to take place.

The Air Gun from Trigger to Target

If the piston were imagined to be fixed in its extreme forward position for some time, then heat would leak away through the cylinder walls, until the temperature became equal to that of the surroundings. The compression would no longer be adiabatic. As the temperature drops, so too would the pressure - even assuming no leakage. It would drop, in fact, to the pressure that would be expected from an isothermic compression of the same magnitude.

We are now in a position to calculate the actual amount of work done on the air as it is compressed by the piston.

Thus, using equation (3):

$$\text{Work done} = \frac{P_2\, V_2 - P_1\, V_1}{n - 1}$$

Using the previous values for pressure and volume:

$P_1 = 14.7$ PSI
$V_1 = 1.964$ Cu. Ins.
$P_2 = 1366$ Cu.Ins.
$V_2 = 0.0785$ Cu. Ins.
$n\ = 1.408$

Thus Work done on the air = 192.235 in.lbs. = **16.0 Ft.lbs.**

We can now see that the total energy required to compress the air to 1366 PSI is 16 Ft. lbs., this must, therefore, be the total amount of energy contained by this air at the stated pressure. It must, however, be noted that at these high pressures, a drop of only 64 PSI. means a decrease of one foot pound in energy.

If the piston remained in the forward position, the full 16.0 Ft.lbs. would be available to propel the pellet up the barrel, but instead, the piston bounces back from this point using up some of the energy. The amount used can be calculated from the same adiabatic equations as before, but this time for an expansion. The calculations are, however, complicated by the fact that as the piston moves back so the pellet accelerates forward up the barrel. We must, therefore, account for the extra volume behind the pellet.

If then the piston bounces back a distance of 0.4 inches away from the cylinder end, and the pellet in this time has reached a distance of 7 inches from the breech.

Then from equation (1):

$$P_2 = 1366 \text{ PSI.}$$
$$V_2 = 0.0785 \text{ Cu.ins.}$$
$$V_1 = \text{Volume in cylinder} + \text{Volume in barrel.}$$
$$= (\pi \times (0.5)^2 \times 0.4 + (\pi \times (0.11)^2 \times 7) \text{ Cu.ins.}$$
$$= 0.5803 \text{ Cu.ins.}$$

Hence: $P_1 = 81.7 \text{ PSI.}$

This is the pressure in the cylinder when the piston has bounced back. Now applying the equation for the work done on or by a gas, equation (3):

Thus work done = 146.6 in.lbs. = **12.2 Ft. lbs.**
(This is the energy given up by the air in its expansion).

Subtracting this from the 16.0 Ft.lbs. that the air contained when the piston was 0.1 ins. from the cylinder end, we obtain the amount of energy remaining in the air: i.e. 3.8 foot pounds.

We must now consider how the 12.2 Ft.lbs. given up by the air has been distributed. From the spring energy curve (**fig.3.1**) we can determine that 1.9 Ft. lbs. was used in compressing the spring 0.4 inches. This was effectively wasted since the compression of the spring served no useful purpose. We also know that when the pellet is seven inches up the barrel, it is moving with a velocity corresponding to an energy of 5.8 Ft. lbs. (see **fig. 9.1**). Thus we are left with 4.5 Ft.lbs. for which we have not been able to account. Probably a good proportion of this has in actual fact been dissipated in heat, since although the process looks adiabatic, in practice some heat will be lost to the cold cylinder. Also at these high pressures only a slight error in the measurement of the piston travel will produce a large error in the energy value.

At the beginning of the chapter we mentioned that the air had a very different function in an airgun which was working in the *popgun* phase relative to its role in the *combustion* phase. In the foregoing pages we have shown how, in the *popgun* phase, it is possible to apply calculations so as to determine how the energy from the spring is passed through the air to the pellet.

In the *combustion* phase, however, the situation is totally different, because, rather than energy being lost in the air, an amount of energy enters the system through the burning of lubricants in the oxygen fraction of the atmosphere. The amount burned at each shot is next to impossible to measure accurately; various suggestions have been put forward over the years such as weighing the gun very precisely before and after each shot. This procedure might appear to be a simple solution, but at each shot a certain amount of unburned oil is exhausted from the muzzle in the form of smoke, also atomised grease will often be found to have followed the pellet up the barrel. However, a fairly accurate answer may be arrived at by experiment and calculation.

In Chapter five we explained how fuel was transported from its reservoirs amongst the coils of the spring and around the piston body to the back of the piston head; and from there to the front of the head. Then, in Chapter two we showed that a normally lubricated rifle, intended to operate in the *combustion* phase, only produces about 45% of the power of which it is capable if its supply of oxygen is removed. This demonstrates clearly that a very crude "diesel engine" system exists that has a reliable and repeatable fuel feeding system and that the combustion of that fuel really does increase the energy that drives the pellet.

The maximum quantity of fuel that can be burned at each shot must be in direct proportion to the amount of air in the cylinder at the start of the stroke; also the maximum amount of fuel that it is possible to burn in 14.4 grammes of air is only 1.0 gramme. Thus the average gun of around 60cc, could only burn a maximum of 80mg of fuel.

However, the fast advancing piston only takes about seven milliseconds to complete its journey, and under ideal conditions the fuel may need three milliseconds in which to achieve reasonable combustion. So unless conditions are exactly right and ignition commences at the exact and critical moment, it is probable that the power from that particular shot will not be as great as it could have been had the timing been better, and there are innumerable factors that can upset the timing.

When combustion occurs the pressure within the cylinder rises faster and higher as shown in **fig 7.3**. The curve would have continued upwards beyond the plateau to form a spike, but the electronic amplifiers clipped the top.

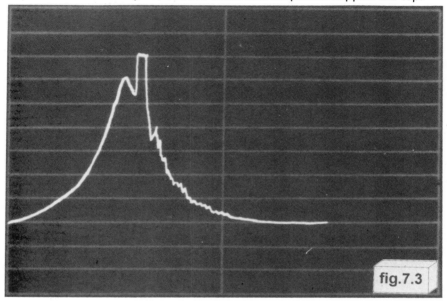

fig.7.3

It has been observed on many occasions that an over powerful spring will not yield the expected increase in pellet energy; this is because the piston is driven forward so fast that there is not enough time for complete combustion to take place, the air and unburned fuel will be ejected from the muzzle and little or no extra energy will be provided so the gun reverts back to virtually operating in the *popgun* phase.

The weight and fit of the pellet also influence the timing, because if the pellet is a tight fit, more pressure must build up before it moves away up the barrel thus allowing adequate time for complete combustion to occur, and therefore more energy to be imparted to the pellet. Nevertheless, like every other factor in airgunning 'an over practised virtue swiftly turns into a vice', and the velocity of a too tight pellet is as disappointing as that of a slack one - the fit of the pellet must be correct before the greatest velocity will be attained.

Any gun can only contain an amount of air equal to the swept volume of its cylinder. The thought struck us *"What would happen if"*... the volume of air present were to be increased slightly by raising its pressure before the shot was fired. No sooner a thought than a deed -a rifle was modified to provide this facility and the cylinder connected to a small compressor via an air port positioned just in front of the cocked piston. A series of shots were fired at increasing pressures from atmospheric up to 75 PSI, but as the pressure was increased the velocity of the shots decreased. Equally well, when the cylinder was subjected to a slight vacuum, low velocities were again produced. In other words the normal conditions of spring power and swept volume are correct for a cylinder full of air at normal atmospheric pressure; if this pressure is altered then in all probability another factor such as spring power would have to be adjusted to compensate. From this it might be argued that a spring gun's power varies with the barometer - it probably does, but by a very small amount.

It is a well established fact that a spring gun will usually propel a light weight pellet at a higher velocity than a heavy one and that this increase in velocity will more than offset the decrease in weight when the energy figure is calculated. This increase in muzzle energy can probably be explained by the very short time during which the pellet is accelerated along the barrel, the lightweight pellet will obviously pick up speed faster than a heavy one. The difference in pellet weight will also, in all probability, have an effect on the all important timing too. On the other hand, a heavy pellet, will usually attain higher energy levels than a lighter one when fired from a pneumatic rifle; this is because a pneumatic releases a far larger charge of air at each shot and therefore is able to maintain a high pressure for greater distances along the barrel to accelerate the heavier pellet more efficiently.

The smoke emitted from the muzzle at each shot is a good, though not perfect, indicator of how efficiently the air is combining with the available fuel. If the piston is supplying the correct and constant amount of fuel for each shot, there will hardly be any smoke at all. Opening the breech and looking through the barrel will perhaps reveal a slight golden vapour obscuring the daylight, if there is no visible vapour then the smell of exhaust will be detectable at the muzzle. The consistency of the velocity under these conditions will be of a high order, whereas at darker smoke densities and higher velocities the consistency will not be as good. Unfortunately that is not the end of the story, we did a series of experiments to determine the relationship between the amount of smoke blown out from the muzzle and the velocity of the shot. We mounted two hydraulic lip seals back to back on a piston in place of the normal head.

These seals are shown in **fig 7.4** and ensured an airtight piston while at the same time not allowing any lubricant to be passed forward from the spring. A pad of leather in the middle of the front seal acted as a reservoir for absorbing the small samples of different grades of oil injected through the transfer port with a hypodermic syringe; the piston, meanwhile, having been pulled slightly away from the cylinder end to allow the fuel free access to the leather pad.

fig.7.4

We very soon realised from this experiment that plenty of smoke was a clear indicator of high velocity though not necessarily good consistency. We therefore assumed that the combustion of oil in a spring gun must be very inefficient indeed; as the density of the smoke left in the barrel fell so also did the velocity, while at the same time the velocity consistency improved. It must be said, however, that some oils gave many more shots than others from the same amount injected into the cylinder, also some samples produced higher velocities than others.

It was also very noticeable during the experiment we mentioned earlier, (the one during which we increased or decreased the air pressure and volume in the cylinder before a shot was fired), that the amount of smoke increased dramatically as the air pressure was lowered. Yet at the same time the velocity fell below normal. This throws light on what actually happens inside the cylinder; first of all the low pressure will suck the lubricant forward past the piston, but as the gun is fired the reduced oxygen available will not support as much combustion as normal and most of the oil will be blown out as smoke. So here we have a situation in which we appear to be arguing against what we have already said, that heavy smoke is indicative of high velocity. The rifle in this experiment was producing plenty of smoke, yet its velocity was very low. The probability is therefore, that there must be a smoke density at which the maximum velocity is achieved; lower powers being generated at densities above or below that value.

Although it was obvious to us by now that the heat and pressure generated within the cylinder by the action of the spring on the air was causing the oil to burn, thereby increasing the pressure still further and adding extra energy to the pellet. We felt we would like to take the project even further and try to measure the extra volume of gas generated by the burn. In our early experiments in this direction we used a cap firmly locked and sealed onto the muzzle of the rifle; provision was made for a toy balloon to be attached to the side of the cap. Upon firing the gun the pellet became trapped inside the cap while the air inflated the balloon. The size to which the balloon was expanded by moving the piston gently along the cylinder was noted before the gun was fully assembled. Firing a pellet at high velocity caused the balloon to expand considerably more than previously. We were initially surprised to note that the balloon first expanded even more, then slowly reduced slightly. This extra expansion was of course caused by the temperature of the air as it left the barrel, as the air cooled its volume slowly reduced until the balloon was slightly larger than it had been when the piston was moved gently by hand.

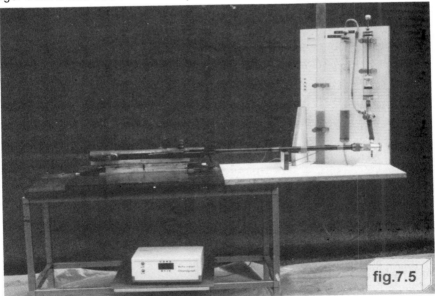

fig.7.5

The Air Gun from Trigger to Target

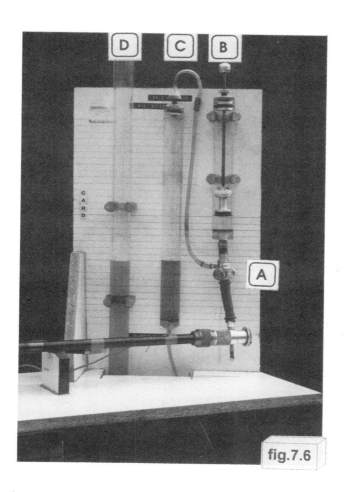

fig.7.6

This rather simplistic experiment indicated that the idea was worth pursuing so we constructed a more sophisticated test bed on which the .22 action could be more permanently mounted (**fig 7.5 & 7.6**). With this equipment we were actually able to gauge the increase in exhaust volume during the *combustion* phase over and above the 98 cm^3 of air the gun contained prior to firing. At the same time we were able to measure the velocity of each shot by means of a chronograph which was connected to two insulated points that projected slightly into the bore.

In practice the flexible connection below the tap **A** is disconnected while the gun is cocked and the pellet inserted, the tap is then set to connect the gun with the cylinder **B** only. The lightweight free fitting piston within the cylinder is then lowered to the bottom before the flexible tube is reconnected and the gun is fired. The pellet travels on past the muzzle to be caught inside the airtight cap, whilst at the same time the air blast blows the piston inside **B** part of the way up the cylinder. The tap is then turned so that the air in the cylinder may be transferred to cylinder **C** when the piston is pressed down. As the air enters the cylinder it displaces the coloured water from a preset level in **C** into cylinder **D** altering their relative levels and therefore pressure. Cylinder **D** must now be moved in its clips to equalise the water so that it is at exactly the same level in **C** as it is in **D**. Under these conditions the pressure of the air in **C** is the same as the atmospheric pressure outside, which of course is the same as the pressure in the airgun at the start of the sequence. Assuming combustion has taken place the volume of air trapped in **C** will be greater than that originally in the gun.

It is now possible to calculate the extra volume of air exhausted from the muzzle because it fills the space in **C** between its present level and original level at the beginning, assuming that the bore diameter of the tube is known.

With this apparatus we could inject any type of oil, grease, water, or other substance directly into the cylinder via the transfer port. We were then able to measure any increase, or even a decrease, in the volume of air exhausted behind the pellet. Injecting anything into the transfer port is never a good practice, and of course we had to suffer the consequences in the form of damaged springs, but it was a price well worth paying in this instance.

Over a long series of shots it became clear that the volume of the exhaust expelled increased in step with a boost in velocity depending upon the substance injected into the cylinder. A figure of 18% extra exhaust was the maximum ever obtained at a velocity of 840 FPS. It must also be said that the increase in volume was a somewhat erratic performance.

At one point during the experiments a small quantity of carbon tetrachloride was injected into the cylinder, its fumes acted somewhat like nitrogen and in stifling any combustion restricted the gun's performance to a low of about 460 FPS which is not far from the low of 426 FPS which we observed from a similar gun operating without combustion during the nitrogen experiment.

Turning then to look at the average high velocities of about 649 FPS produced by this gun in the *combustion* phase when there was a normal supply of lubricant present in the cylinder, and from which it was producing an extra 12% of exhaust, we can compare these with the maximum high of 636 FPS obtained during the nitrogen experiment. We felt that the sets of high and low figures were close enough to confirm that a spring gun requires a supply of lubricant in order to produce its maximum velocities, also that the increase in volume of exhaust is an indicator of the gun's performance in the *combustion* phase.

It is curious, however, that some lubricants tend to give higher velocities than others. This is surprising because the calorific value of a fuel (that is the heat energy they can give out on burning) is near enough the same for most oils. The answer probably lies in the manner in which the lubricant is mixed with the air as the piston flies forward. If it forms droplets or mist it will burn more efficiently than one which remains as a thick film.

Chapter 7 - The Air

Chapter 8
THE TRANSFER PORT

The transfer port, that is the small hole that connects the cylinder to the barrel, must be looked at in two ways, both in its function as a simple air passage in the *blowpipe* or *popgun* phases, and separately as a combustion chamber in the *combustion* or *detonation* phases. We will consider the port first in its role as a transfer passage between the cylinder and the barrel.

Over the years the size of the port has been a constant source of interest and curiosity. Rifles have been ruined by over enthusiastic use of drills in the hope that a larger diameter would increase the power of the gun. A larger port has always appeared to be the gateway to higher velocities; but like every other factor in airgunning a compromise between conflicting factors must be struck. The difficulty lies in establishing the exact nature of the factors involved.

There are three main variables to be considered when investigating the geometry of the port. **(i)** *Its diameter.* **(ii)** *Its length.* **(iii)** *Its shape.*

Before discussing these points, however, let us first consider exactly what happens when the air rushes through the passage. As the piston streaks forward, pressure is built up behind the pellet, the pellet then releases its grip and accelerates off up the barrel at the moment of peak pressure in the cylinder (if it is a correctly fitting pellet). As it accelerates, the pressure behind it immediately falls, the high pressure air in the cylinder then rushes through the port to equalise the lost pressure, hence an airflow has been created from the cylinder to the barrel. This pressure difference must be maintained to preserve the airflow. But, to accelerate the pellet further, the flow must increase, and this can only be achieved by a continuously increasing pressure difference between the pellet base and the cylinder.

When the pressure on the barrel side of the port drops to about half of the cylinder pressure , a condition known as "critical flow" is set up. At this point the airflow through the port is brought to a constant velocity and cannot be further increased without raising the cylinder pressure. But the cylinder pressure is already falling due to the backward movement of the piston and the forward motion of the projectile, this means, therefore, that the pellet can no longer be accelerated. It may however be pushed along at a constant velocity, since although the flow rate cannot be increased it will not necessarily decrease.

The only way in which the rate of flow may be improved upon is by raising the cylinder pressure or, maintaining the existing pressure for a longer time by holding the piston in the forward position. Our efforts in this direction have already been described and it is clear that it is "easier said than done".

When critical flow is reached, flow impeding shock waves form in the transfer port, because under these conditions the velocity of the air flow is equal to, or greater than that of the local speed of sound. It must be remembered that *the local speed of sound* varies considerably depending upon the pressure and temperature within the port as the air passes through it at the moment of firing and may be vastly different to the normal accepted figure of about 1100 feet per second.

It should be clear from the foregoing that it is of vital importance that there should be as little restriction as possible to the air flow so that the pellet obtains the maximum acceleration before critical flow is reached. Let us now discuss the three factors mentioned earlier, since maximum airflow depends upon the format of this port.

The diameter of the port is somewhat dependent on the calibre of the gun, if the port were larger than the calibre there would be a probability that the pellet would be drawn back into the cylinder. To determine the most efficient port size for our particular gun, we adopted a system of trial and error. This involved the drastic operation of machining out the existing port to a diameter of about three eighths of an inch. We then machined a series of interchangeable ports each identical, apart from their bore diameters, which were machined to individual sizes, ranging from $^1/_{16}$" up to $^{11}/_{64}$". The rifle chosen for all these experiments was of the break barrel type, it was, therefore, possible to use an "O" ring to seal the breech and at the same time hold the false port in position. The rifle was not very large by today's standards having a bore of 1" and a stroke of $2^1/_2$"; therefore its swept volume was only 1.96 Cu.ins.

With this system we were able to experiment with each port size in as many experiments as we wished whilst ensuring similar conditions. The following table lists the port diameters together with the average velocities obtained with each size, the calibre being .22".

Port Diameter (ins.) (Port Length $^3/_4$")		**Average Velocity** (Feet Per Second)
1/16"	(0.0625)	334
5/64"	(0.078)	338
3/32"	(0.094)	420
7/64"	(0.1094)	424
1/8"	(0.125)	428
9/64"	(0.141)	425
5/32"	(0.156)	423
11/64"	(0.172)	414

From these results it is clear that the optimum port diameter in this case is about $^1/_8$". Either side of this diameter the velocity immediately becomes lower, for smaller diameters this is easily understood, since a small hole offers far more resistance than a large one which, in turn, will allow a greater mass rate of airflow through it. The reason for the velocity falling when using a port diameter greater than $^1/_8$" is less easily understood. It is probable that much above this figure an unacceptable amount of "lost volume" is produced, resulting in a decrease in the final pressure, and therefore, a reduction in the accelerating force behind the pellet.

At a later date we repeated the experiment with a larger rifle as part of an in depth study which included varying the input energy as well as the port size. In this instance the piston diameter was 1.18" with a stroke of 2.56" giving a swept volume of 2.8 Cu.ins. The optimum port diameter was again $^1/_8$" which surprised us, however since the port was 1" long the increase in lost volume obviously counteracted the increased swept volume. We used two springs, one with a power of 36 Ft.lbs., and the other 45 Ft. lbs. The lower powered spring produced higher output powers, thus a higher efficiency, re-affirming our previous observations that greater spring power does not necessarily yield greater velocities.

"Lost volume" is a term we use to describe the volume of air contained by the transfer port and other holes or recesses in the piston head, also the small space inside the pellet itself. It is in fact space which, though unavoidable, creates inefficiency in the system. Taking an extreme case to illustrate the point, suppose that the lost volume amounted to a large fraction of the total volume swept by the piston. The piston would then accelerate forward and hit the end of the cylinder before there was enough pressure build-up to arrest it, neither would the pressure generated be great enough to start the pellet off up the barrel. It will be noticed that in the first gun the maximum port diameter tested was $^{11}/_{64}$", this was because any further increase in diameter resulted in the piston actually hitting the end of the cylinder. In other words the spring had enough power to compress all the air within the swept volume into the lost volume, allowing the piston to strike the end wall.

The length of the port is far more difficult to alter or experiment with, but it is obvious that the shorter it is the better, as it then produces less lost volume. Also being short there is less resistance to air flow due to wall drag on the air as it rushes through the passage. Over the years we have seen the design of rifles evolve until in many recent models the port length has diminished to nothing. It is worth bearing in mind, however, that there is nothing special about the port, it is in reality, only an extension of the barrel backwards behind the pellet. If the port is eliminated altogether by designing the breech so that the barrel seals directly into the end of the cylinder, then the beginning of the barrel takes the place of the port throttling the air flow to the back of the pellet as it accelerates up the bore.

Early rifle makers often drilled the port at an angle so that it joined the centre of the barrel to the centre of the cylinder. This was probably done in the belief that the air would flow faster from the centre of the cylinder rather than from one side. Present day practice seems to indicate that there is no difference, because angled ports have been abandoned. However, any slight advantage that might have been gained by taking the air from the centre would be eliminated by the increased length of the port also interference with the air flow at the sharp edged ends of the hole.

Air, like any other fluid, has viscosity, viscosity is the property of a fluid which makes it resistant to flow. Compare treacle emerging from a tin to the flow of water from an upturned bucket, also the viscosity of the treacle will diminish as its temperature rises and it will flow faster. Of course air is not as viscous as water at normal temperatures and pressures, however it has, like all gasses, the surprising property that its viscosity increases with temperature and also with high pressure. Since, in the main, we are dealing with high pressures and temperatures, energy losses in the air due to this action could be significant.

In order to get a practical idea of what happens at the port, it is helpful to imagine the air to be a liquid. With this thought in mind, it is not difficult to remember how the flow of a stream is impeded as it flows over a rocky bed; the sharp edged stones form waves and eddies that restrict the smooth passage of the water. In a similar way, most of the rifles that we have looked at have a sharp edge at the entry to the port, since it is simply a drilled hole. Obviously there is nothing better than a sharp corner for upsetting the flow of a fluid and causing flow restricting eddies; in fact, it would be true to say that a sharp corner is the opposite of streamlining. This edge, is therefore, a part of the system where energy is certain to be lost.

Again, practical experiment was the only method open to us to investigate the energy losses at the transfer port. We took one of the false ports and shaped the entry to a bell mouth; this immediately increased the velocity of the experimental gun by seven feet per second. Other guns that we have modified in this respect have produced better results than this, which goes to prove that the shape and size of the port is individual to each type of gun.

So, what is best? Well, very often the designer of any spring air gun is "between the devil and the deep blue sea" in this area. What is required, is the shortest possible length of optimum diameter port with a smooth lead-in for the air, and, incidentally, a polished surface throughout, this smoothness is of course important whatever the size or shape of the port. Unfortunately, however, it is not always possible for the port to be short without losing physical strength in that area, especially in the design of barrel cockers.

The production of a bell mouth at the entry end of the port is a refinement that is not often encountered on mass produced rifles. From a purely theoretical point of view the best possible shape for a transfer port would be a bell mouth at the entry followed by a venturi; that is a hole which contracts at the centre, then opens out again to a diameter that corresponds with the entry to the breech. However, after going to the trouble of making such a device, we were disappointed to find that the practical advantages were insignificant.

The breech sealing washer on some early break barrel models is fitted into a recess cut directly into the end of the transfer port. There is of course a danger here that some energy will be lost at this point, since it is unlikely that the airflow will remain smooth as it passes through the washer. The situation is made worse because the washer is likely to be compressed when the action is closed thereby reducing the diameter of the hole.

One well known make of tap loading rifle at one time had a funnel shaped end to the cylinder, giving a streamlined flow of air from the cylinder into the barrel. The piston had a cone shaped end to coincide with the angle of the funnel. Another great advantage of this system was that the transfer port was exceptionally short since the tap was positioned directly at the apex of the funnel. The whole point of the design was that efficiency losses in this area were kept to a minimum. Unfortunately, one can only presume, the manufacturing costs outweighed the increase in efficiency.

The question of transfer port efficiency was the subject of an in depth investigation carried out at Bristol University by Messrs. Maddox and Rowson. They showed that it is possible, under certain circumstances, for the air in the cylinder, for an instant to attain a negative pressure; but only for an instant. If the pellet has moved a short distance along the barrel when the piston bounces backwards it may pull some of the air that has already passed through the port back into the cylinder. This did not altogether surprise us, because we had occasionally found particles of lead adhering to the piston head and cylinder end of rifles that we had serviced. We had often wondered how they had got there and had come to the conclusion that perhaps they had been sucked in from the breech as the rifle was cocked. However this phenomenon will only be observed with rifles working in the *popgun* phase, in the *combustion* phase there is no possibility of air being drawn back into the cylinder.

Maddox and Rowson also showed that once a certain air speed through the transfer port is reached the flow becomes supersonic and the port becomes choked by shock waves. After that the air cannot go through any faster with the result that pressure builds up in front of the piston. On occasions we have fired sporting rifles without a pellet in the breech and have noticed that a very loud crack is produced and the barrel is left full of smoke. In the light of the work of Maddox and Rowson it is clear that once the port chokes up, any further pressure build may become high enough to cause combustion to take place and the rifle behaves just as though there was a pellet in the breach. However, since the airflow through the port under these conditions is supersonic, the noise from the muzzle will be the familiar crack of a supersonic bullet or perhaps, a whiplash. In this instance the sound is increased by the combustion of the oil, leaving the barrel full of exhaust.

If, on the other hand, the gun is small, or its power and dimensions do not lend themselves to the conditions we have just described; then in all probability there will be insufficient pressure build up in front of the piston to arrest its travel. The piston will then violently hit the cylinder end.

Turning now to the part played by the transfer part in the *combustion* phase. In this instance the port ceases to be a corridor for the passage of hot, fast moving, high pressure air, instead it becomes a combustion chamber for the fuel ignited by the heat and pressure generated by the spring and piston. We investigated, as far as we could, the combustion within the port by inserting three perspex rods **A**, **B** & **C**.into the combustion area (**fig 8.1**). The first **A** was positioned in the end wall of the cylinder. Its inner end had been filed and polished in such a way that it resembled a tiny periscope looking along the bore directly at the approaching piston. The next was placed directly into the port itself, and the third entered the barrel just in front of the pellet when in its normal position prior to firing. Each $^3/_{16}$" diameter rod was shaped where it enters the port or barrel, its end surface blending perfectly with the surrounding contours so as to form neither an obstruction nor a void. Port **B**. appears to be larger than those either side of it, this is because we had expected to be able to examine the light in more detail if the viewing end of the rod was made like a lens. In the event the light pulse was made exceptionally visible by the lens, but little extra information was discernable.

The photograph (**fig.8.1**) shows the ends of the rods, together with the illumination seen by a camera as the gun fires. The phenomenon demonstrated by this picture is not so much that a bright flash occurs as the fuel ignites, but that the ignition has occurred mainly within the transfer port. Also, since port **C** is placed in front of the pellet's head and is only uncovered as the pellet leaves, it is very interesting to note that such a bright light is visible at all at that point. This clearly illustrates that the fuel is still burning as the pellet moves along the bore, and probably does so for the first few inches.

The exact nature and timing of compression ignition has, over the years, been the subject of intense world wide investigation by mathematicians and diesel engineers such as Sir Harry Ricardo in this country. However, their work involved more precisely controlled machines than our somewhat whimsical guns; but it is never the less of great interest to read their books on the subject, since they serve to enforce the arguments and principles involved in the *combustion* phase.

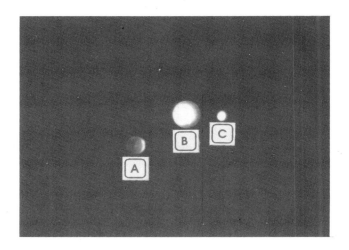

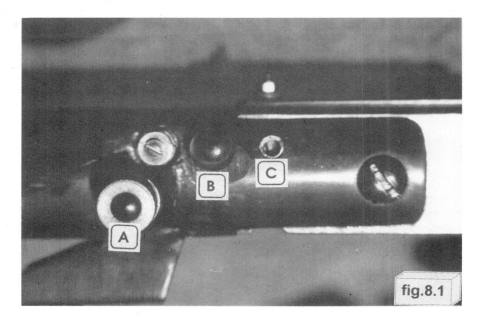

fig.8.1

Chapter 9
THE BARREL

When we speak of the barrel of an air rifle, we mean the whole tube extending back from the muzzle to the breech, the point where the pellet is seated ready for firing. Although it may seem unnecessary to make such an obvious definition, we have done so because we want to make it quite clear that we have included the section of the bore that holds the pellet before "blast off." It is, in fact, this small part that helps to determine the consistency of the rifle, but more of this later, let us first have a look at the controversial topic of the barrel length.

Barrel Length

We went to a great deal of trouble over the study of barrel length since much of the current thought on spring airguns was being derived from firearm principles. This comparison is completely unscientific, as are most other comparisons between firearms and airguns. In the case of the firearm the projectile is under acceleration along the whole length of the barrel; this total acceleration is arranged by matching the quantity and type of propellant in the cartridge to the length of the barrel. The propellant having been carefully designed to burn itself up within the time the projectile is in the bore. This being so, the gasses produced by the combustion of the propellant keep up a nearly constant pressure on the base of the bullet giving it enormous energy.

Unfortunately, the spring airgun is severely handicapped in this respect because there is only very limited energy available to accelerate the pellet and that is virtually all imparted to it in the first five inches or so of the barrel. After this distance, the pellet neither loses nor gains speed until it has covered a further twenty five inches or so, after which it begins to slow down due to friction from the barrel wall and also because of the volume of air that the pellet is having to move ahead of itself along barrel. From this it is clear that a spring airgun with a long barrel is not more powerful than its shorter barrelled counterpart, though it must be said that a sporting rifle operating in the *combustion* phase may benefit from a longer barrel than one that is working in the *popgun* phase.

The **fig 9.1.** shows the typical acceleration of a .22 pellet up a barrel. From this diagram it can be seen that the pellet was accelerated during the first five inches of its travel only, the remainder of the journey was accomplished at a steady velocity. The reason for this stable velocity is that critical airflow has been set up through the transfer port due to the reduced pressure in the cylinder. This critical flow as already mentioned in a previous chapter, means that the air can now only flow at a certain speed, hence the pellet is only pushed at a steady rate and not accelerated.

Acceleration of Pellet

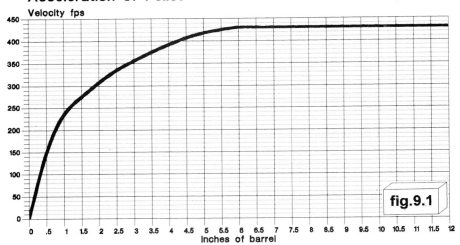

fig.9.1

The graph in **fig 9.1** was arrived at by the use of the very odd looking barrel shown at the bottom of **fig 9.2.** which had holes drilled in its wall at one inch intervals all along its length, into each of these holes an insulating bush was screwed and each bush carried a small screw that was pointed at the end and could just enter the bore. With this strange device it was possible to make contact with the pellet at any desired point along the barrel, as the pellet passed any screw that had been adjusted into the bore, electric contact was made between the screw and the pellet at that point and therefore with the barrel itself. Coupling this to a chronograph it was possible to establish the time taken for pellets to traverse various sections of barrel. This experimental piece of equipment could be coupled up to any number of sections of the extendable barrel shown in the top of **fig.9.2.** By this process, we were able to study barrels of up to five feet in length. At these extended lengths, the velocity had fallen to an utterly useless figure, but the experiment was well worth while since it proved beyond doubt that a long barrel is not the key to high velocity in a spring rifle.

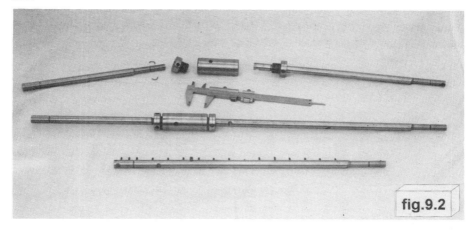

fig.9.2

The opposite situation exists in the case of pneumatic rifles. Here there is usually more than adequate air available to accelerate the pellet all the way along the bore, in many instances an even longer barrel could be used to advantage, but then the rifle would not only look wrong, but its balance and handling would be next to impossible. In cases where quietness is important, the excess air must be vented into a silencer, air that might have been used to further accelerate the pellet had there been more barrel in which to do it.

Pellet Fit

During our experiments with differing barrel lengths we were made very aware that the fit of the pellet and therefore the shape of the breech are crucial factors in the power of the rifle. Once we realised the importance of this point, we set about investigating it in great detail. First of all we checked what we call the "static" pressure required to start the pellet down the barrel through various breech shapes. We connected short lengths of 0.22 barrel to a hand operated oil pump in such a way that we could increase the pressure behind the pellet very gradually, whilst at the same time being able to watch the rise in pressure on a gauge. As the pressure reached the point at which the pellet released and moved forward up the tube the pressure gauge needle fell, the maximum pressure obtained in each case being noted.

Each short length of the 0.22 barrel had a different shape machined into its breech so it was not difficult to compare the static release pressure of the various shapes when fitted with standard pellets. It was also possible to investigate the pressures attained by pellets with expanded or collapsed tails. It must, however, be emphasised that this is an experimental static starting pressure only, and that the hydraulic test was done on a much slower time scale than the one witnessed inside the gun. The actual starting pressure (dynamic) being approximately three times this value, mainly due to the inertia of the pellet.

After checking the static starting pressure each barrel was mounted on the experimental gun and its performance measured with the chronograph. The results, all the average of 20 shots, are recorded below:

Breech shape	Static Pressure (psi)	Velocity (fps)
Sharp right angle breech.	374 psi.	371 FPS.
Slight radius at breech.	444 "	434 "
45^0 Chamfer at breech.	442 "	373 "
60^0 Chamfer at breech.	399 "	390 "
Slow taper into barrel.	308 "	292 "

It is clear from the results with this particular gun that a static pressure of 440 PSI. is required to produce maximum velocity in .22 and is best attained by a polished radius at the breech. This optimum shape is illustrated in **fig 9.3.** It is possible to have a pellet too tight in the breech, resulting in it not starting until after the peak pressure is reached, producing a lower muzzle velocity. This fact can be proved by expanding the skirts of pellets beyond reasonable dimensions, then checking their velocity.

The reason that a sharp right angled breech produced a low pressure and therefore low velocity was because, instead of re-forming the tail of the pellet it sheared a ring of lead from the skirt, this shearing of the tail must obviously require less force than re-forming it into the bore.

We concluded from these experiments that at the moment of firing, the tail of the pellet must first grip the end of the bore, then as the pressure behind it rises, the skirt collapses until it becomes the same size as the bore, at which point it releases and accelerates up the barrel with the maximum pressure behind it. The importance of the pellet's grip on the breech prior to firing is lost if the pellet is first forced through a sizing die. These tools appear on the market from time to time together with glowing accounts of their advantages, normally of course they only serve to reduce the rifles velocity through reduction of the pellet's tail diameter, though in some instances, it must be said, they can be of service where the pellet in its normal state is totally unsuited to the barrel or the power of the rifle. The breech shape is of less importance in the case of a pneumatic, because in most instances the front of the bolt pushes the pellet forward into the rifling making it a perfect fit before the gun is fired, virtually in the *blowpipe* phase.

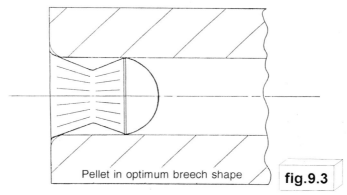

Pellet in optimum breech shape   **fig.9.3**

An added bonus arises from the correct breech formation; the final velocity becomes far more consistent. We found the variation over a number of shots to be 2% with the correct shape, while the others showed a figure in the region of 6%. This was obviously a worthwhile improvement, it is probable that the 2% variation was due to differences between the pellets.

The polished radius that we found to be so efficient is not easy to achieve when the rifle is fitted with a loading tap. Taps have always had a tapered hole into which the pellet is dropped, as we have shown in the above table a taper is about the worst possible shape with which to achieve efficiency and consistency. Taps may also decrease efficiency, because the pellet will inevitably take up a position at the barrel end of the hole thereby increasing the lost volume of the transfer port. However, tap loaders are steadily giving way to more sophisticated loading systems such as magazines, the BSA rotary breech, or the system adopted by Weihrauch on their classic model 77 where the pellet is loaded directly into the end of the barrel after the cylinder has been withdrawn.

Break barrel designs are not quite so popular now that scopes reign supreme, because there is always the worry that the barrel may not take up exactly the same position, shot after shot. The break barrel system was the most widely used in the early days of popular spring guns, but on expensive rifles it was replaced by an under lever and tap because the early breech joints were liable to leak, or quickly became loose. Also, the fact that the barrel had to be used as a lever reduced their popularity further because they could become bowed.

The Muzzle

Turning now to the muzzle end of the barrel. It is vital to the rifle's accuracy that the muzzle is mechanically perfect, there must be no burrs, patches of rust or enlargement, though it must be said that this last blemish is unlikely to be found in an air rifle. Firearm barrels are often cleaned using a pull-through which is purely a piece of cloth attached to a length of cord. If the cord is allowed to drag on the bore as it passes the muzzle it will eventually enlarge it through "cord-wear" ruining the accuracy of the rifle.

Quite obviously the muzzle is the most important section of the barrel as far as accuracy is concerned, it is responsible for imparting the final direction to the pellet. If the end of the barrel is not square to the bore then the pellet will take off in the wrong direction. To check this point we deliberately machined a muzzle at an angle of about fifteen degrees to see what would happen. We were surprised to find that although the pellets left the muzzle at approximately the same angle as the new face, they flew quite accurately producing a remarkably small group on the target, which had to be placed well away from the normal line of the barrel.

It is vital that the pellet must be a firm fit in the bore as it leaves the rifle otherwise pin point accuracy will be lost and it is for this reason that many manufacturers compress the last three quarters of an inch or so at the end of the barrel to form a 'choke'. Although the term choke is better known in shot gunning circles where the reduced diameter at the muzzle holds the shot in a tighter pattern as it leaves; we airgunners have borrowed the term. However, the degree of reduction in an airgun barrel of perhaps 0.001" is nowhere near that used in a shot gun, where the reduction may be in the region of 0.030" or more.

The reason for choking airgun barrels is to ensure that the pellet leaves the barrel at a tight spot. It is no discredit to any barrel manufacturer to say that his barrels are not perfect and need a choke to improve their performance. Whatever system of barrel manufacture or rifling is employed the bore diameter is bound to vary by very small margins over its entire length; each barrel will be different and the large and small diameters will not occur at the same places in every example. If every barrel has a choke pressed into it after all the other machining operations are complete, and if that choke makes the bore slightly smaller than any previous tight spot, then the pellet is bound to leave at the tightest point along the barrel's length. In an ideal world all barrels would be perfect, their diameters would be exactly the same all along their lengths, there would be no blemishes anywhere within them to upset the pellet's travel. In practice however, this is next to impossible to achieve, at least not at a realistic price. Neither is it correct to say that just because a barrel is choked that the choke is there to disguise a poorly made item. Many manufacturers choke their barrels to make them less pellet fussy and to gain more uniform results from a wider range of pellets. They probably find a choke to be an advantage because as the pellet moves along the bore its diameter is reduced by wear, therefore the pellet is smaller when it leaves than when it started; even though the bore is perfect. So the choke compensates for this reduction in diameter.

In the early days of choked barrels, the choking was often excessive, in the region of 0.004", this robbed the pellet of much of its power. On several occasions we bored out that section without any apparent loss in accuracy but with a large improvement in power, perhaps we were lucky in that the pellet still left at a tight section of the barrel; that was a chance we took.

As a quick experiment to check on the advantages of a choke we once deliberately reversed the barrel and loaded the pellet into the choked muzzle end. The pellets flew in all directions; obviously the choke had reduced them to the point where they became a very slack fit in the remainder of the bore, rendering them totally inaccurate. This simple experiment demonstrated how accuracy partly depends on a tightly fitting pellet, particularly as it leaves the muzzle.

Rifling

The history of rifling is in itself a fascinating story. Ever since its true value was first established in about 1800, there have probably been more experiments carried out trying various groove shapes and rates of twist than with any other part of a gun. No doubt fortunes too have been made and lost during the search for perfection. Some of the designs were fascinating; rifling whose pitch slowly increased so that the bullet's spin rate was increased gradually as it travelled along the bore. Rifling whose depth increased as it approached the muzzle was also tried, the object of these strange designs was usually to prevent the bullet "stripping" the rifling as it left the breech. Stripping appears to have been a major worry in the early days when all bullets were made of lead, and not metal jacketed as now. It was thought that if too much powder was loaded behind them they would not grip the rifling correctly. They would then travel up the barrel as though it was smooth bored, leaving the muzzle without spinning. This argument is hard to follow when it is realised that the early gunmakers fully understood that a bullet expands into the rifling as the pressure developed by the burning propellant increases.

It is perhaps difficult to understand why rifling, once thought of, did not immediately become a standard on all barrels. There were, however, other factors working against its advantages; fouling in the barrel caused by the burning of black powder caused the early barrel makers much frustration. Also, the lack of an acceptable breech loading system to defeat the problems of muzzle loading, held up the development of successful rifling systems.

However, in 1909 Dr. F.W. Mann wrote a book called "The bullet's flight from muzzle to target." It has ceased to be considered as a major work in the field of ballistics because it is mainly about large calibre lead bullets, which of course are now well out of date. It is, nevertheless, a work of great importance to air gunners, because his methods of investigating bullet flight are still applicable to our lead pellets. Many of our own studies have been based on his experimental techniques.

Dr. Mann devoted most of his working life to the study of bullets' flight, he did more controlled experiments with lead bullets than anyone else in his day. He clearly demonstrated that stripping, in normal circumstances, is a myth. He even forced a bullet through a riffled barrel until only a quarter of an inch of it was left in the bore, he then gripped the protruding front end of the bullet and twisted it expecting it all to rotate in the bore, yet in fact, the bullet twisted off flush at the muzzle leaving the remainder intact in the barrel. This simple experiment, and others, proved beyond doubt that even a modest depth of rifling is capable of imparting the very small amount of energy to the bullet that is required to make it spin.

Chapter 9 - The Barrel

It is important to realise that a spinning pellet contains two forms of energy, together with the linear kinetic energy with which we are all familiar, the pellet also contains "rotational energy" that is the energy imparted to it by the rifling. Calculating the magnitude of spin energy is somewhat more complicated than linear kinetic energy, it involves determining the pellet's moment of inertia, which of course partly depends on the speed at which the pellet is spinning together with its structural form also its diameter. However, as far a our normal pellets are concerned, the amount of rotational energy involved is negligible when compared with its kinetic energy.

Dr. Mann mentions that throughout all his work with rifles, much of which involved stopping bullets in snow or oiled sawdust, he never saw a bullet which had stripped. We would endorse this statement, in all our experiments, where pellets have had to be stopped in flight for examination, we have never seen one that has stripped. It just does not happen.

Even after all these years a perfect rate of twist has yet to be agreed upon, perhaps it never will; each barrel maker still has the flexibility to use his own ideas on the subject. Yet the direction of the twist of the rifling appears to be standardised as right hand, that is, the pellet rotates in a clockwise direction as it moves from the breech.

Looking down the barrels that we have used during our work, we find rates of twist anywhere between one turn in thirteen inches and one turn in thirty four inches. We have heard of experimental twist rates well above and below these values, yet none proved to be exceptionally accurate. Looking at the twist rates in firearm barrels the variation seems to be as wide as that in airguns.

It must be remembered that air guns firing the popular shuttlecock shaped pellets do not totally rely on the gyroscopic effect of the rifling to keep them steady in flight, they rely on the pellet's shape too. In all probability shuttlecock shaped pellets were first made in the hope of increasing the accuracy of early ball firing, smooth-bored airguns. Some bright airgunner must have noticed that a shuttlecock always flies nose first and miniaturised their shape in lead. Even today it is surprising just how accurate a smooth-bored gun can be when firing a modern pellet at short range. So our pellets may be said to be dual stabilised, firstly by the spin imparted to them by the rifling and secondly by the air as it passes over them once they leave the muzzle; like the shuttlecock.

An interesting calculation shows that a pellet travelling at an average velocity of 550 FPS from a barrel rifled at the rate of one turn in sixteen inches, will be spinning at a rate of about 25 thousand revolutions per minute, an enormous speed. But, after it has covered a distance of thirty yards, it will only have revolved about seventy times.

The shape of the grooves and lands of the modern air rifle barrel are fairly standard (**fig 9.4**), the lands being the sections between the grooves which grip the rifling. In most instances the lands and grooves are of equal width, but their number varies anywhere between six and twelve. Again the manufacturer makes his own choice on the number. The depth of each groove seems to be fairly constant at between 0.002" and .003" for both .177 and .22 calibre, but in the case of .25 the depth may rise to about 0.004"

Normally the diameter at the bottom of the grooves is the same as the quoted calibre, therefore the diameter measured at the tops of the lands is smaller than the calibre by twice the rifling depth. Individual manufacturers, however, may deviate from this standard, this path is normally followed for commercial reasons, such as trying to make the barrel only suitable for a non standard brand of pellet. As we see it this is long term commercial suicide and renders no service to air gunning in general. Understandably air gunners are unwilling to be tied to any one make of pellet and will eventually shun both the non standard rifle and its odd pellets.

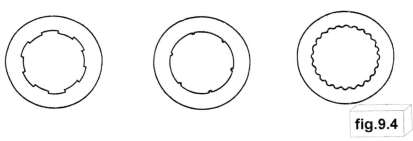

fig.9.4

We said earlier that the lands are usually the same width as the grooves, but Weihrauch always make their .22 barrels with a somewhat unusual rifling form. The grooves here are very wide while the lands are little more than sharp ribs spiralling along the bore. This system has many advantages, there is very little deformation of the pellet when the rifling is printed onto it, also the air seal is exceptionally good, especially in instances where the air pressure is perhaps not high enough to expand the tail into the corners of more conventional rifling.

There is in fact another type of rifling called polygroove, here the rifling resembles numerous small corrugations. There are far more grooves than on normal systems, and often the grooves are hemispherical, leaving sharp lands in between to grip the lead bullet. Polygroove is not very common these days but in earlier times it was used on many large calibre rifles and invariably on air canes.

A similar system is called microgroove, it consists of very many shallow grooves, so shallow in some instances that it is very difficult to see them without a magnifying glass. They spin the pellet perfectly satisfactorily and do far less damage to it than more conventional rifling patterns where deep rifling, together with a choke, may cause the outside of the pellet to resemble a circular saw. **Fig 9.5.** shows two similar pellets that have been pushed through differing barrels. The one on the left has been through a tight barrel, that was also choked. It has obviously been damaged to the point where its accuracy will suffer. The one on the right was a correct fit, the head rested on the lands perfectly, while the rifling was gently printed on the tail.

fig.9.5

Referring back to Dr. Mann, he demonstrated that if a lead plug covered with emery was spiralled backwards and forwards along a smooth bored barrel, the bullets would pick up perfectly on the shallow scratches. They would then leave the muzzle, spinning just as though the barrel had been rifled in a more conventional manner.

Chapter 9 - The Barrel

We followed Dr. Mann's instructions and scratch rifled a smooth bore .22 barrel. The pellets emerged without a blemish, it might even be said they were of a better and more even shape than when they started. However, it must be admitted that in this instance the accuracy was not as good as that from a normal barrel, but then ours was not choked. It would seem to us that some form of microgroove rifling holds plenty of promise for air guns. Although it might not be popular with newcomers who would like to see positive spirals when they look down the bore.

Barrel vibration

In the field of firearms, barrel vibration is often blamed for inaccuracy. High speed photography has been used to examine this phenomenon and shows that a rifle barrel vibrates and wriggles about like an excited snake as the bullet travels along it. This is not surprising when one considers the huge pressures generated by the burning propellant as it forces the tight fitting bullet along the tube.

We investigated barrel vibration to see if it was the cause of inaccuracy in airguns. We were interested only in vibrations caused by the pellet itself while it was in the barrel and immediately it left the muzzle; we did not want to be concerned with any vibrations set up by a spring and piston so we used our *pneumatic projector* in this instance. Later on, in the chapters on pneumatics, we will describe the projector in more detail, but for now it may be accepted as being a very solidly mounted pneumatic rifle whose barrel may be left unsupported over the majority of its length.

We mounted vibration transducers on the muzzle of a breech mounted barrel so that any vibration would be picked up and displayed on an oscilloscope. A slight thump with a hand anywhere on the barrel would cause the trace to move violently, yet firing the gun produced very little reaction. By causing the pellet to break a circuit carried by a pencil lead, as it left the barrel we could determine whether the small amount of vibration we had seen occurred before or after the pellet had left the muzzle.

This experiment showed an insignificant amount of vibration before the pellet left, but that the small amount of movement we had seen, occurred after the pellet had left. This after exit vibration could have no effect on the accuracy of the shot.

Various other experiments were embarked upon to cross check the first, also to assure ourselves that vibration played no part in the production of large groups. In one instance we clamped a heavy lathe chuck onto the muzzle, on another occasion we mounted the barrel in soft rubber rings, but the effect on the group sizes was negligible. The important factor always appeared to be the combination of barrel and pellet, later on we realised that in fact the combination of pellet, barrel and velocity have a far greater influence on the size of the group than any amount of vibration from a rifle in good condition.

Lubrication

The cleaning and lubrication of barrels is an area that has always generated great controversy. A correctly greased spring powered rifle will always keep the barrel sufficiently lubricated by virtue of the small amount of grease and oil vapour which follows each pellet through the bore. On the other hand a pneumatic rifle, or a spring rifle working in the *popgun* phase, will not lubricate the barrel at all. Marksmen using these rifles often advocate the use of a small amount of spray lubricant to wet their pellets at the start of a competition. In years gone by nobody ever cleaned the barrels of their air rifles. Recently, however, the quality of rifles and pellets has increased to the point where their potential accuracy is very high indeed, and a clean, slightly oiled, barrel has proved to have great advantages. Cleaning rods fitted with soft brushes are used occasionally to remove the grease and lead shavings which may remain in the rifling. But, like so many other things in airgunning, *"To over do it is to undo it."* Too much cleaning of the barrel, especially with harsh brushes or uncoated rods will do far more harm than good.

Defects

Occasionally barrels, either through accident or misuse, become bent. If this damage is not immediately visible it can be the cause of endless frustration, especially if a scope is fitted because there is doubt as to whether it is the barrel or a misplaced scope which must be blamed for the missed shots. It is not difficult to pull a barrel back straight provided the damage is not concentrated in one spot, as when the trigger of a break barrel has been released before the breech has been fully closed. In that instance the barrel is often severely kinked at the point where it enters the breech block. However, if the barrel is removed from the cylinder it can usually be straightened by gripping it in a vice between pieces of softwood then gently pulling it back true with the aid of a straightedge.

Chapter 9 - The Barrel

Barrel makers employ a system called "shading" to check the straightness of their tubes, this is a highly skilled trade in which the reflection of a broad black band fixed across a window, is viewed through the barrel. By tilting and rotating the tube the shadow is caused to move gently and smoothly along the bore, an experienced eye can than detect any errors which may be corrected immediately.

The examination of the bore and rifling of a barrel may best be undertaken by looking through from each end against a bright light; an eye glass is of great assistance as it will reveal the condition of the bore to a considerable depth, areas up to about three inches from the end can be brought into sharp focus, any blemishes or deep scratches may be clearly seen by this method.

It is possible to examine the form and condition of the rifling at either end of a barrel if it is oiled inside and then blocked with cloth at a convenient distance from the end. The portion to be examined should then be warmed and filled with molten sulphur. Once it has cooled down the plug can be easily pushed out for examination with a magnifying glass. We have found that sulphur gives a better image than the more traditional lead. Be careful not to overheat the sulphur or it will turn to a substance like chewing gum.

Airguns suffer from a curious phenomenon, if a series of shots are fired and then the breech is held near the mouth and gently blown through, the velocity of the next shot will be higher than that of the previous ones. There are various possible explanations for this curious performance, perhaps blowing through the bore removes the heavy vapours which may impede the next shot, alternatively the action of blowing may cause a film of moisture to be deposited in the bore which lubricates the next shot. This suggestion seems to be the most likely since blowing the fumes out from the muzzle end does not cause an increase in velocity.

However, as a final thought whilst on the subject of barrels, it is interesting to consider for a moment the gun that is all barrel and very little else, the blow pipe. The incredible feats of range and accuracy with which they are credited are made even more surprising when one realises that it is difficult to produce even one pound per square inch pressure when blowing into the pipe. Yet tribesmen are reported to be able to kill birds and monkeys at considerable ranges, in some instances without the use of poisoned darts. The secret being that the blow pipe relies on its length and the size of the hunter's lungs to produce a useful velocity. Whereas the spring operated air rifle employs a tight fitting pellet to produce a small volume of highly compressed air behind itself, the blow pipe missile is a very loose fit in the bore to enable the hunter's lungs to maintain a constant acceleration all the way up the pipe. In other words, it relies on a large volume of air at a steady low pressure rather than a small volume at high pressure.

No doubt the pipe length has been developed to the maximum to suit the size of the hunter's lungs, whilst at the same time keeping the volume small by reducing the calibre to the smallest practical size of dart. The weight and construction of the dart itself will also have evolved by trial and error, but the success of the final combination is world famous.

Chapter 9 - The Barrel

Chapter 10
RECOIL

In the years since we wrote *"The Air Gun from Trigger to Muzzle"* the characteristic possessed by every gun, called recoil, has become more important than ever to the air gunner. This deepened interest in recoil has partly been generated by the almost universal use of scopes, because it can damage them, or at least move them along the cylinder losing their correct alignment as they go. Though without a doubt the most important reason for the wish to understand recoil and hopefully diminish it, is that it works against the very high levels of accuracy attainable by the rifles and pellets available today.

However, the type of recoil that causes the damage to scopes only occurs on rifles where the energy is stored in a spring or gas ram, and since that recoil is not true recoil at all, we will come back to it later.

True Recoil

True recoil is mainly caused by the acceleration of the pellet from its state of rest to the high velocity it reaches as it exits the muzzle. It is best examined against the background of Newton's third law of motion which states: *"To every action there is an equal and opposite reaction"*. Very often enthusiasts, both airgunners and firearms owners alike, will argue about the point at which the recoil occurs, some believing that it happens at the moment the shot leaves the muzzle, others that it develops only after the shot has left.

The action of recoil can be demonstrated very clearly by two people standing face to face on an ice rink, if one of them tries to push the other away they will both move in opposite directions at the same moment, the lighter person moving faster. From this example the true sequence of recoil is not difficult to understand, if one imagines a monster projectile equally as heavy as the gun itself, it then becomes clear that the action of recoil must begin immediately the projectile starts it journey along the barrel. At this moment the gun will be pushed backwards simultaneously as the projectile is pushed forwards. The fact that in the case of our airgun the projectile is far lighter than the gun itself makes no difference to the timing, only to the magnitude of the forces involved.

There are in fact three causes of recoil in a pneumatic air gun, the most important of which is that caused by the weight of the pellet. It is important, not because it is always the greatest, but because it occurs while the pellet is still in the barrel and can therefore effect the accuracy of the shot. The second is that caused by the rocket effect of the air blasting out of the muzzle after the pellet has left, finally there is a very small amount of recoil caused by the weight of the air in front of the pellet as it is accelerated along the bore. This last factor may be ignored as far as airguns are concerned, there is neither enough weight nor velocity in that small volume of air for it to influence the final recoil figure.

The rocket effect is perhaps surprising, but if one forgets about the bullet for a moment and imagines a firearm to be a true rocket which has a large amount of propellant loaded in the breech, then it is not difficult to realise that as the propellant charge burns and expands inside the barrel there will be an out-rushing of very energetic gasses whose reaction in a rocket would send it skywards. In the case of the airgun, the reaction generated by the expanding air forces the gun backwards into the owner's shoulder instead of upwards into the air. In fact, the air may be considered to be another projectile behind the original pellet, but of course it will not have the same weight as a pellet though it may be travelling faster. Its effect on the total recoil figure can be surprisingly great as we will explain later.

Earlier, we said that the recoil commences at the same moment as the pellet leaves the breech, this implies that it must cease when the pellet leaves the muzzle. Yet we have just shown that recoil arising from the jet effect occurs after the pellet has gone, we must therefore split the recoil into two parts, but in so doing we are also splitting hairs, especially where airguns are concerned. It is perhaps simpler to magnify the situation by first looking at a system containing greater energy, the shot gun. When a sportsman fires he feels a considerable kick driving the butt into his shoulder, the recoil he experiences is the combination of the three factors that we have already considered together with the extra recoil produced by the wads and cards which go to make up the weight of a shotgun's charge. Later in the chapter we will show that in fact the recoil generated by the rocket effect may amount to about two thirds of the total recoil energy. Bearing this in mind it is obvious that the only part of the recoil which can effect the accuracy of the shot must be that generated by the projectile itself, the remaining rocket effect can have no influence on the pellet once it has left the muzzle. The same situation also arises in the case of very powerful pneumatic rifles whose rocket effect again makes up a considerable proportion of the total recoil.

Chapter 10 - Recoil

The magnitude of the pellet generated recoil depends upon three factors, the weight of the projectile, its velocity and the weight of the gun. This immediately explains why even a powerful pneumatic produces very little recoil. The pellet is light, the velocity relatively low and the gun is very heavy when compared with its projectile. Since the weight of the gun is such an important factor in the calculation of the recoil it must also be remembered that the shooter becomes part of the system, the better the gun fits its owner and the firmer it is held the lower the movement of the rifle will be because its stock is well supported and therefore appears heavier. Though of course this argument is more applicable to firearms than air rifles because the forces in such shot guns are much greater.

Let us now consider the first of these three elements in further detail, that is the gun's reaction to the forward acceleration of the pellet. By Newton's third law, the pressure driving the pellet forward up the barrel exactly equals the pressure driving the gun backwards causing the recoil, and they both act only for the time the pellet remains in the barrel. By the principle of the conservation of linear momentum; the motion of the pellet forward in feet per second multiplied by its mass is equal to the rearward motion of the gun in feet per second multiplied by its mass.

If:

The mass of the pellet = M
The mass of the pellet = m
Velocity of the gun = V
Velocity of the pellet = v

Then by the conservation of momentum: $m \times v = M \times V$

Since mass = $\dfrac{\text{Weight}}{\text{Acceleration of gravity}}$

Thus we have: $\dfrac{w}{g} = \dfrac{W}{g}$

Where · W = Weight of Gun. w = Weight of pellet.
(g is constant and the same for both gun an pellet.)

Then:
$$w.v. = W.V. \qquad \ldots\ldots\ldots (1)$$

Thus: $V = \dfrac{w.v.}{W}$

We may now calculate the velocity of the recoil, and hence the energy imparted to the gun by the reaction from the pellet's acceleration.

Weight of gun (W)   = 6.625 Lbs.
Weight of .22 pellet (w) = 0.00214 Lbs. (15 Grains)
Velocity of pellet (v)   = 430 fps.

Substituting values:

$$V = \frac{0.00214 \times 430}{6.625} = 0.1389 \text{ Ft./Sec.}$$

From the equation for energy:

$$E = \frac{WV^2}{2g}$$

Thus again substituting values:

$$E = \frac{6.625 \times (0.1389)^2}{2 \times 32.16} = \mathbf{0.002 \text{ Ft. Lbs.}}$$

Being practical sort of people, we could not let the recoil investigation depend solely upon a mathematical solution, so we set up the spring gun to give us some practical results. We suspended it by two cords from a beam in such a way that the barrel was level and remained so during the recoil swing. We then fixed a pointer to the side of the rifle and placed a scale in a fixed position beside it; from then on it was a simple matter to photograph the scale and pointer at the moment of firing to determine the exact amount of recoil. We fired the gun by means of a solenoid mounted on the butt, the solenoid being positioned at right angles so that its movements had no effect upon the recoil readings.

Upon firing, the gun swung backwards and forwards like a pendulum and in so doing lifted slightly. It is the amount of this vertical movement as the gun swings back that we need for our further calculations because it is the 'feet' in the Foot Pound calculation. If we know the weight of gun and the distance through which it lifts we can calculate the amount of energy in foot pounds transferred to it by the shot. Since the lengths of the supporting cords are known and the amount of the swing measured, the application of some more mathematics will show how much energy is being expended in recoil. It will be obvious from equation (1) that a light 0.177 pellet will produce less swing, and therefore, less recoil, than the heavier 0.22 pellet. From our experiments we found that a 0.22 pellet weighing 15 grains produced a swing of 0.4 inches on our rifle weighing 6.625 Lbs. when it was suspended by cords 22 inches long. So by the use of Pythagoras the vertical distance through which the rifle was lifted during its backward swing can be calculated (**fig 10.1**).

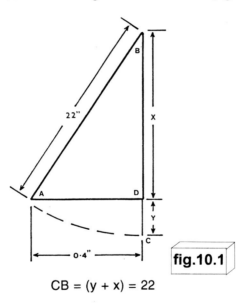

fig.10.1

$$CB = (y + x) = 22$$

Therefore: $$x = 22 - y \qquad \text{... (1)}$$

Since triangle ABD is a right angled triangle then: $AB^2 = BD^2 + AD^2$

Thus: $$22^2 = x^2 + 0.4^2$$
Hence: $$x^2 = 22^2 - (0.4)^2 \quad \text{...(2)}$$

Using eqnt. 1...

$$x^2 = (22-y)^2$$
$$x^2 = 22^2 - y^2 - 44y$$

Substituting from equation 2...

$$22^2 - (0.4)^2 = 22^2 - y^2 - 44y$$
or
$$y^2 - 44y + (0.4)^2 = 0$$

Solving this quadratic equation gives us: **y = 0.0036 ins.**

In the case of this particular rifle the vertical lift amounted to 0.0036 inches, or 0.0003 feet. This figure may then be multiplied by 6.625 pounds which is the weight of the rifle to give a figure of 0.002 Ft.lbs.

Thus, this very small figure is the amount of energy used in pushing the rifle backwards and upwards, or its total recoil energy, established by experiment. It is so small that it may be neglected when considering energy losses as a whole. It is, however, interesting to note that there is no difference between this figure and the calculated value arrived at earlier, which was for the reaction due to the acceleration of the pellet alone. One might expect some small difference between the two figures produced by the rocket effect of the air escaping after the pellet left the muzzle. The very small reaction caused by this effect can obviously only be determined experimentally and cannot be detected by the shooter because he feels it as part of the total recoil.

Rocket Effect

Out of curiosity we then decided to see if we could isolate the very small rocket effect by a practical experiment. We made a muzzle brake and fitted it to the end of the barrel, this device occasionally used by the military to reduce the recoil of their rifles, reverses the flow of gasses from the muzzle. In our version, the brake was an extension of the barrel, increasing its original length by about two inches. Three small ports were drilled into the bore at an angle of about 30 degrees to the barrel. The blast of escaping air would then be deflected backwards in opposition to the rearward moving recoil, forcing the gun to move forwards during the brief moment during which the pellet was in the extra two inches of barrel. However, the results were disappointing, and probably rightly so in view of the relatively low pressure and volume available at the muzzle of a spring rifle. We had hoped that we would have been able to detect a slight difference in the swing of the suspended rifle between the two conditions, muzzle brake fitted, and no brake; but the readings were all too close to one another to make any discernible difference. Such is the life of investigation !

Having studied the recoil of a spring gun in some detail we realised that the investigation was not complete without carrying out the same experiment with a pneumatic rifle. We therefore suspended the working parts of our *projector* (**fig.15.5.**) from cords of the same length as those we had used earlier in the spring gun experiment, we also added lead blocks so that its weight was the same as the spring gun earlier, allowing direct comparisons to be made between the two guns.

On firing, the pneumatic rifle swung through a far greater distance than the spring gun. Since the recoil distance was so great we did not use calculation to resolve the amount by which the rifle lifted as it swung, instead we drew an arc of twenty two inches radius on a piece of graph paper and then directly read off the amount by which the rifle lifted as it moved backwards.

As already stated the results we obtained for the total recoil in the pneumatic were considerably higher than those originally obtained for the spring rifle under the same conditions, we now measured energies of 0.012 Ft.lbs. instead of the earlier 0.002 Ft.lbs. This increase led us to presume that the extra recoil must be caused by the rocket effect, (far more air being released after the pellet leaves the muzzle of a pneumatic than from a spring gun). A long series of experiments showed up a surprising number of facts about recoil as it appears in pneumatic rifles. Shots were fired with velocities high enough to give between six and forty five foot pounds of muzzle energy, in some instances no pellet was loaded, in other instances a silencer was fitted while on other occasions the same muzzle brake which we had used earlier was again employed.

At normal airgun powers, that is up to about twelve foot pounds, there was very little difference in the recoil energy of the pneumatic whether or not a silencer or muzzle brake was fitted. If a pellet was not loaded the recoil was reduced by figures between a half and two thirds of the 0.012 Ft.lbs. figure established when a pellet was fired.

However, at much higher powers the situation changed considerably; for instance firing a 14.4 grain pellet at a muzzle velocity of 1134 FPS, that is 41.1 Ft.lbs. the gun swung back far enough to indicate a total recoil of **0.56 Ft.lbs.**

Fitting a silencer at this power reduced the recoil to **0.37 Ft.lbs.**, while the muzzle brake reduced it to **0.126 Ft.lbs.** and firing it without a pellet produced **0.39 Ft.lbs.**, a figure again near to two thirds of the maximum established when a pellet was fired. This must therefore be approximately the energy generated by the rocket effect.

In the case of the silencer, the reduction in the recoil results from the expansion of the air inside the body of the silencer. The size and design of the silencer must therefore influence the reduction of the recoil. A silencer with a large expansion chamber will obviously reduce the pressure of the outgoing air to a greater degree than a small one, therefore the rocket effect must also be diminished.

Calculating the pellet generated recoil energy for the pneumatic, a figure of **0.0128 Ft.lbs**. was obtained when firing a 14.4 grain pellet at 1134 FPS from a rifle weighing 6.62 Lbs. The large difference between this calculated figure and the figure of **0.56 Ft.lbs.** observed, must be the amount of energy imparted to a rifle by the rocket effect.

Before leaving this discussion on true recoil it might not be out of place to take a quick look at a very popular firearm; the 12 bore shotgun. Give or take a pound or two it can weigh approximately the same as an air rifle, calculation shows that a shotgun weighing $6^1/_2$ Lbs. will generate 16.9 Ft.lbs. of recoil energy when discharging 500 grains ($1^1/_8$ oz.) of shot at 1,200 FPS. An alternative source suggests that in fact the observed recoil of a shotgun to be in the region of 31 Ft.lbs., nearly double that of the calculated figure. The two figures again serve to emphasise the enormous increase in recoil caused by the rocket effect which we previously calculated for our pneumatic.

Spring Recoil

Returning now to the scope damaging recoil of which we spoke earlier; this is caused by the piston and its driving force, whether it be a spring or gas ram. Assuming the gun to be cocked, that is the piston is at the start of its stroke and the spring compressed behind it. At the moment the trigger is released the spring accelerates the piston forward very rapidly. However, as Newton explained earlier, *"To every action there must be an equal and opposite reaction".* This means that as the piston is forced forwards the gun must be forced backwards by the expanding spring, the rearward movement is fairly energetic because the piston is usually heavy and its acceleration fast. Also, about half of the total weight of the spring must be combined with that of the piston adding to the rearward force acting on the rifle's body. This addition is made because many of the front coils are accelerated forward along with the piston by the coils at the back end of the spring.

The result of the combined forward movement of the piston and spring is that the gun is first thrown backwards into the shoulder of the shooter, but at about the peak of the gun's rearward acceleration the piston and spring are suddenly stopped by a cushion of compressed air built up between the front of the piston and the back of the pellet. The violent forward blow given to the rearward moving gun by the sudden arrest of the spring and piston causes the gun to change direction within a very small interval of time. This hammer blow may be further compounded because the piston will continue to bounce back and forth several times, driven by the remaining energy in the spring and the air compressed in front of its head. It is this sudden reversal of movement, rather like a whiplash, which causes the scope, or indeed anything else attached to the rifle to be thrown backwards, often with great force. The magnitude and frequency of these forces vary with each type of gun and also with the weight of the pellet, but the greatest variation to the pattern of the vibrations in any one rifle is caused by combustion, if this is violent the forces and vibrations transmitted to the scope may be catastrophic.

Various attempts have been made to calculate the magnitude of the force acting on the scope when a spring gun is fired. This force must be stated in terms of g, in a similar manner to the forces acting on the pilot of a fast fighter aircraft as he turns, or pulls out of a dive, or those acting on a motor car and driver when it stops suddenly. Whichever way we looked at the problem there were factors involved which we could not resolve by calculation in a satisfactorily accurate manner. We called on Roy Elsom to help us, he had collaborated with us in the writing of our previous book *"The Airgun from Trigger to Muzzle"* and understood the difficulty of the problem. He is now a professional vibration engineer and has access to sophisticated equipment with which g forces may be measured directly.

We built up a .22 HW 35 rifle weighing eight pounds to give velocities of about 550 FPS and then mounted an accelerometer on the end of a steel bar clamped in the scope mountings. The bar weighed 1 $\frac{1}{4}$ Lbs. to represent the weight of an average scope. Firing 15.5 grain pellets showed a g reading of about 25. We then fitted the dummy scope to an HW80 rifle which weighs nine pounds, this rifle gave lower g readings at higher velocities, 660 FPS. producing about 20g. Injecting oil into the cylinder induced a few violent detonations with velocities in the region of 870FPS and 60g. The value of g was not mirrored by the velocity, like every other factor in airgunning there were other variables influencing the result. A detonation of any magnitude always increased the g value, firing without a pellet did not necessarily reduce its value, but a gentle combustion shot at about normal velocities of 660 FPS gave lower g figures. We came to the conclusion that in instances of correct combustion the expanding gasses slow the piston down in a controlled manner to reduce the violence of the piston's reversal.

If an object is subjected to an acceleration of 2g its weight is doubled during the time of the acceleration, we also now know that the acceleration caused by the sudden changes in direction may induce forces of 60g in each component of the scope. It is now clear that our steel bar could weigh up to 70 Lbs. at the moment the gun fires, so one has to ask whether the 'insides' of the scope can stand having their weight instantaneously multiplied by 60, or more, when the trigger is released. It would not be out of place to mention at this point that the spring was irreparably damaged by this treatment.

Of course a pneumatic, or a firearm, does not punish a scope in this manner because the pneumatic only produces pure recoil. In the case of a firearm, if the scope mountings are not firm then as the gun moves backwards the scope will inevitably move forwards towards the muzzle, not backwards as occurs in a spring gun.

Twist Recoil

Another subject, which although not directly connected with recoil may be mentioned here even though its effect amounts to next to nothing. It is the twisting reaction applied to the rifle by the pellet as it sets off up the rifled barrel. As we already know, any action must be accompanied by an equal and opposite reaction, therefore as the pellet is forced to spin there will be a reaction trying to rotate the barrel and therefore the whole rifle in the opposite direction. True, but because the pellet is so light relative to the rifle, little energy is required to set it spinning and the reaction is negligible. In military terms this twisting may produce unique problems, especially in recoilless rifles.

Chapter 11
LUBRICATION

The lubrication of spring guns is a most difficult subject. The reader will have already gathered from previous chapters, where combustion has been discussed, that the combustible qualities of a lubricant may have more influence on the performance of the gun than its lubricating properties. The combustible properties of any oil or grease vary widely depending upon their constituents and conditions within the gun. We will therefore, first look at the requirements of a spring gun; those of a pneumatic are vastly different and we will leave them until we discuss rifles working on this system in chapter 14.

It is not unreasonable to start off by describing the action of an oil or grease in any machine. When spread between two close fitting surfaces oil forms a very strong film, it keeps them apart and allows them to slide freely over each other riding on the film. If there is no lubrication at all between two load carrying surfaces they will tear into each other as they move. If enough force and pressure are applied they may in fact become permanently welded together as they go, this action being commonly known as "seizing." Smooth surfaces obviously respond to the action of lubrication better than rough ones, so the better the polish and lubrication of the working surfaces of an air rifle the more pleasant it will be to operate. The rifle will also produce more consistent velocities and will last far longer.

It could be suggested that any oil or grease can fulfill the requirements of the actual lubrication of a spring gun since there are few moving surfaces that are under very heavy pressure. When considering any lubrication problem it is the pressure per unit area which is important, rather than the total load. Probably the pressure per unit area is greatest on the cocking link joints, often these pins are very small for the load they are expected to carry during the brief cocking stroke, therefore they need plenty of care in the form of regular lubrication. The breech hinge pin on a break barrel rifle also needs consideration, not so much because it is heavily loaded during the cocking stroke - it has a far greater area of contact than the link pins; it leads a hard life because it has to withstand much of the whiplash jerk as the cylinder is thrown backwards and forwards by the piston and spring. It suffers in exactly the same manner as the scope mounts which transmit the jerk from the cylinder to the scope, instead the hinge pin must transmit it to the barrel. A film of heavy grease here protects the hinge from damage.

At the same time it is vital that the side faces of the breech joint are kept well lubricated. These faces must carry out two opposing requirements, they must hold the joint rigid when it is closed yet at the same time must allow it to open and close without undue stiffness as the rifle is cocked. These conflicting conditions are usually met by keeping the hinge pin pulled up tight, resulting in heavy loading between the faces of the breech block and the inside faces of the cylinder's forked end. Over the years, rifle manufacturers have used various systems to reach a compromise. Each manufacturer employing his own system of shims, washers, dished washers or even springs to make a joint which is firm yet free to move without undue stiffness. Lubrication of this joint must be carried out at regular intervals. Cheaper rifles very often have neither washers nor threaded pins, relying only on a hardened pin. The manufacturers are obviously prepared to accept that once the joint becomes slack the whole rifle will also be too badly worn to be worth repairing.

Probably the area of a spring gun that suffers worst when lubrication is ignored is the top of the piston's skirt at the trigger end. This small area is pressed hard against the cylinder wall as it slides during the cocking stroke, if it is not adequately lubricated deep scores will soon appear in both surfaces causing grinding noises as the rifle is cocked. Eventually it will become impossible to cock the gun when the piston and cylinder seize together.

As we have already said each of these areas could be adequately served, as far as lubrication is concerned, by virtually any oil or grease. It must be understood however, that in most instances a grease is really only an oil held in a binder, like water in a sponge. Once the oil has dispersed, only the binder will be left in the form of a hard soapy substance, usually black with age and filth. In some instances the binder itself will have some lubricating properties because it contains graphite or perhaps molybdenum disulphide, a favourite substance for airgun lubrication.

When considering the lubrication of any machinery, especially when it is fast moving, it must be realised that there is such a thing as "grease drag," or in the case of oil, "oil drag." This works to the detriment of the machine. The classic case of this situation is an over greased fast running ball or roller bearing, the excess grease is then churned through the cage and rolling elements of the race, in so doing it absorbs energy and therefore becomes hot. The heat builds up causing the bearing to expand and generate friction and more heat which under extreme conditions may cause it to seize solid.

Obviously a thick grease will produce this condition faster than an oil or a thin grease.

As far as airgunners are concerned the problems associated with grease drag apply only to the pistons of spring guns, and we touched on the subject in the chapter on pistons. The amount of drag caused by grease, or even oil, is increased by the size of the area of the surfaces in contact and also by their proximity to each other. The pistons on early rifles were usually shaped like cotton reels, they had broad flanges at either end while the centre was undercut. This undercutting served two purposes, it provided a space for grease, while at the same time reduced the area in close contact with the cylinder walls and therefore the ill effects of grease drag. Yet in spite of this early experience, many modern guns are made with a parallel sided piston without any relief at the centre of the body.

The inevitability of a cocking slot running along most of the length of the cylinder means that the greased spring is open to the air, also allowing dust or dirt into it. It is a far cry from the sealed spring units so often found on the steering or suspensions of modern cars. The air may cause the grease to oxidise, while at the same time the dust and dirt will combine with it to form a sludge; which is not beneficial to the smooth working of any gun.

The lubricating properties of any grease are a minimal requirement when used in a spring gun, it requires far more specialised characteristics before it is successful. As we have already described, the grease is open to contamination by dust and moisture, it must be resistant to these. Some greases when left open to the air will quickly discolour and disintegrate, obviously these brands must be avoided. The grease must not become thin on a hot day, it may then become too fluid and run out into the stock. The lubricating oil in the grease must be firmly held in its binder, if it is not, then over a period of time the oil will slowly be drawn away from its binder to other parts of the gun, usually into the wood of the stock, leaving in its place a thick soapy sludge.

By far the most important property of a lubricant for a sporting spring rifle is its combustibility, or better, its value as a fuel. The number of lubricants on the market is legion, new ones appear every year like spring flowers, by next year they have vanished and gone ! Each combines with the air upon compression in a seemingly different manner; although, as we have already described it, the action would appear to be simple enough - the piston compresses the air, a certain amount of the oil is burned up in the available oxygen to give the pellet extra energy, and that is it.

In practice, however, there can be a vast difference in performance depending on the oil; we usually describe lubricants as being "active" or "passive." Active, if they readily cause the gun to operate in the *combustion* phase. Others, usually heavier greases, are more passive and may be used in high power rifles with less likelihood of the gun becoming unstable, that is producing a series of high and then low velocities, or even moving into the damaging *detonation* phase.

The difficulties encountered in the quest for a perfect lubricant for a spring gun stem from the very high temperatures generated as the piston completes its forward stroke. These temperatures may exceed one thousand degrees centigrade in a powerful rifle, but only for an instant. No oil or grease, either mineral or synthetic will withstand these temperatures without burning; even the piston head itself may be scorched and any sharp corners melted or burned away by the superheated air.

These high temperatures and pressures in a spring gun may be accurately compared with the situation within the cylinder of a diesel engine. In the engine the combustion of the fuel is brought about by the high pressure and temperature generated as the piston moves forward. The fundamental difference between the two machines is that in the engine the fuel is injected into the cylinder at a critical and precise moment, usually just as the piston is approaching the end of its compression stroke. Whereas in the gun, the fuel in the form of lubricant, is collected by the piston as it moves forward and is then burned in a haphazard manner as it is ignited by compression. In fact the actual combustion mainly occurs within the transfer port, as previously discussed (see chapter 8).

Dry powder lubricants such as graphite or molybdenum disulphide can provide the necessary lubrication under these conditions of heat and pressure but they are totally unacceptable in a spring powered gun. As part of our studies of the *combustion* phase we tried lubricating a rifle solely with graphite powder. Of course without combustion the velocity fell to a very low figure but also the mechanical noise rose to unacceptable limits, it sounded like a 'box of washers' because there was no longer a film of oil between the moving surfaces.

A lubricant which is too active in a particular rifle will usually make its presence felt by excess noise, recoil and perhaps smoke from the muzzle. It must not be forgotten however, that the same lubricant might be very successful in a gun of lower potential. If the piston head is badly worn or damaged, allowing too much fuel to be transported into the compression chamber, the gun will become very erratic, some shots will be of very high velocity while others will be very low, dark smoke will certainly be very noticeable. A very good parallel to this situation is a worn lorry diesel engine that is being fed on an over rich fuel/air mixture, it will travel along leaving a trail of smoke behind, whereas a new engine will only leave a slight trail of vapour and familiar smell of exhaust. A spring gun is exactly the same, if it is supplying itself consistently with the correct amount of a successful fuel there will be hardly any smoke at all. Opening the breech and looking up the barrel will perhaps show a slight golden vapour obscuring the daylight at the other end. Even if there is no visible vapour, the tangy smell of exhaust will be detectable at the muzzle.

The matter of testing differing types of fuel was discussed in more detail in the chapter on *'the air'*, but it is next to impossible to foretell exactly how any lubricant is going to perform in a particular rifle. We come back to the best solution of all airgun problems; trial and error. The final choice depends on many factors; primarily what is expected of the gun. Other factors such as spring power; type and fit of the piston head, all go to determining how well a lubricant is going to serve its purpose.

Obviously if a gun is to be used in paper target competitions at relatively short ranges, it should be lubricated very sparingly with a passive lubricant so that combustion does not take place and the shot to shot velocity is held at a very constant, but relatively low figure. At the other end of the scale, if the rifle is to be used for field sports at greater ranges where maximum velocity is required, a more active type of lubrication is required. In between these two extremes there are a host of situations each requiring a different gun and lubrication to suit the circumstances.

The consistency of the grease applied to the spring should be neither too thick nor too thin, if it is thick it will impede the movement of the piston and spring, if it is too thin it will slowly creep out away from the spring and into the stock. The consistency of very thick cream would seem about right.

To combat the twin obstacles of contamination and oil migration it is advisable to add new lubricant often, but a little at a time. Occasionally the whole gun benefits from being stripped, washed out completely and a fresh supply added. The precise time between these clean-outs is impossible to predict because it all depends on the amount of shooting that is done; also how and where the rifle is stored. If it is stored conventionally, that is upright, resting on its butt in a warm place, there is the likelihood that the oil will migrate backwards out of the cylinder and into the stock. Conversely, if it is stored in a less orthodox manner, lying on its back in a cooler place the lubricant will stay in place without deteriorating for a much longer time.

The amount of grease required by any particular rifle depends again on its application. Those which must operate in the *popgun* phase obviously require less than those used for field sports. In our experience a gun should be assembled with no grease or oil at all in front of the piston, a small amount then smeared on the skirt of the piston, especially at the trigger end. The main body of the grease should be spread on the spring before it is inserted into the piston, but this quantity should never be so great that it is forced out of the piston and into the cylinder when the rifle is cocked.

Several times in this chapter we have mentioned the multiplicity of spring gun lubricants on the market. Although some are better than others in individual rifles, we do not believe that the perfect grease has yet been developed. Perfection, it would seem, is an impossibility in one product because it could not give satisfaction in all guns. Perhaps a series of about five could cover the whole range of requirements, they would vary in degrees of "activity" between being totally passive right up to being very active. The enthusiast could then choose for himself the one most suited to the needs of his sport and his rifle.

Inevitably the power of a rifle that is operating within the *combustion phase* will slowly deteriorate as the active components of the lubricant are consumed. Often this will lead to disappointment on the part of a newcomer to airgunning, especially when he buys his first new rifle; after a few months it may not have the same power that it did at the beginning. Certainly the spring will be blamed for this loss, but in fact, the spring will in all probability, be exactly the same length as when new. The cause of the trouble is of course that the active elements of the grease will have dispersed to other parts of the gun or will have passed across the piston's head to be burned in the cylinder. In other words the rifle can be said to be, *"Out of fuel"*. It is for this reason that we always advise that a rifle should be lubricated *"little and often"*. Not all the products of combustion will be driven up the barrel in the form of smoke, any soot that is left behind will combine with unburned fuel to form a gummy deposit on the piston head and even in the transfer port too, neither of which will have a beneficial effect on the rifle's performance. Some lubricants have the property of maintaining a longer useful life than others, this is a characteristic that can only be determined by experience with the product in question.

It is a curious thing that if for some reason a rifle is stripped and the piston withdrawn then immediately replaced it will be found that the velocity value will have altered considerably, usually downwards, only recovering itself after many shots have been fired. We mention this phenomenon to illustrate just how sensitive is the performance of a spring gun to alterations in what we call the "pattern" of the lubricant. The word pattern has always seemed to us to be the most descriptive way of portraying the characteristic of the grease as they combine with the mechanical idiosyncrasies of the rifle to produce a certain velocity. If the pattern of the lubricant is disturbed the whole character of the rifle will be upset until it settles down again many shots later.

Since silicone oil first became readily available it has been sold for the lubrication of airguns. Great care must be exercised with this oil since it is not suitable for the lubrication of metal surfaces rubbing together under pressure. It is fine for lubricating plastics and leather in contact with metal, such as piston heads, but the tail of the piston must be lubricated with a more conventional material, though of course the two will eventually mix with each other to form a compound of doubtful lubricating abilities. Silicone, however, is an exceptionally good oil for protecting the metalwork of a rifle from moisture and the corrosion that so often results from handling.

It has always seemed to us to be pointless to use a multitude of lubricants in a spring rifle, one on the spring, another on the piston and perhaps a third on the trigger, and so on. Inevitably the violent movements within the cylinder as the rifle fires will mix all the various oils and greases into one which may not be successful in providing the consistency of velocity that is required. Since, as we have already said, any grease or oil is capable of providing adequate protection against friction, there seems little point in complicating an already difficult situation with more variables.

Any rifle is likely to suffer from what is known as *"spring-twang"*. This is the inevitable result of suddenly releasing a coiled spring within a confined space. The noise is of little importance beyond being irritating in most situations, but to the hunter it may make all the difference between getting off one shot or two at a group of quarry. It is possible to reduce the noise by fitting a plastic sleeve on either the inside or outside of the spring. However the normal cure for this noise is a grease which is heavy enough to dampen the spring's uncoiling vibrations. This cure must be used with caution because of course it may also reduce the speed of the piston, which is not beneficial to velocity.

Inevitably any excess lubricant which is not burned at the front of the piston will be blown along the barrel to lubricate the pellet. On the other hand the insides of a pneumatic need so little lubrication that the small amount of oil blown along the barrel may be discounted as pellet lubrication. Experience with pneumatic rifles has shown that to obtain the best accuracy and consistency from these rifles it is advantageous to slightly lubricate the pellets themselves before loading them.

Over the years many people have suggested that the performance of a spring rifle must be influenced by temperature, something we had never ourselves observed. The only possible reason for this variation we thought might stem from an increase in the efficiency of combustion of the available fuel at higher temperatures. To test this, we wound a heating coil around the cylinder and very soon found that there was no detectable difference in velocity either in the *popgun* phase or in the *combustion* phase at any reasonable increase in temperature. However once the cylinder became so hot that it could not be touched the gun moved into the *detonation* phase and became totally uncontrollable. Since this sort of temperature could never be experienced under normal conditions we did not take this study further. We also cooled the cylinder by injecting refrigerant into a jacket surrounding it. Having left the rifle cocked so that the air inside had plenty of time to cool, we again found that the velocities were much the same as for a gun at normal temperatures.

Although, from what we have just said about lubrication and the important role it plays in the successful working of a spring gun, we may have given the impression that such a gun is not reliable and must be continually serviced to keep it shooting in a satisfactory manner. This is in fact far from the truth, they are not really as difficult to manage as might be suggested. The system is very reliable and consistent as long as it is fully understood. There are far more spring guns manufactured each year than all other systems put together, this fact alone speaks worlds for their success.

Chapter 12
EFFICIENCY

The mechanical efficiency of any machine is the ratio of the useful work got out of it, to the work put into it. This ratio is usually expressed as a percentage, thus:

$$\frac{\text{Work output}}{\text{Work input}} \times 100 = \text{Percentage efficiency.}$$

In this book we have considered the work input of a spring air rifle to be the amount of energy that is contained in the spring after the gun has been cocked, and not the amount of energy that is required to compress the spring into its cocked position. This energy will always be greater than that in the spring, because there is always a loss through friction at the pivot and slides. We have not made a study of the losses in the mechanical linkage system since individual manufacturers employ slightly different mechanisms of varying mechanical efficiency and the loss would be of very little interest anyhow.

The work output is the amount of energy contained by the pellet as it leaves the muzzle, this is called the muzzle energy and, like the spring's energy, is measured in Foot Pounds.

Assuming that the energy stored by the spring has been determined and when fitted in the gun can contain 20.4 Ft. lbs. then:

Energy available from the spring   = **20.4 Ft. lbs.**
Muzzle velocity, using 14.5 grain pellets   = **430 FPS.**
Therefore from **fig 1.1** the muzzle energy = **5.9 Ft. lbs.**

Thus the efficiency = $\dfrac{5.9}{20.4} \times 100 = \mathbf{29\%}$

This figure immediately strikes one as being remarkably low, yet all the rifles that we have tested have produced about the same figure, between 25% and 35%. The variation depends mainly upon the physical dimensions of the gun.

We shall now closely examine each of the areas of energy loss previously mentioned throughout the book, and also one or two other escape routes. It is the sum of all these losses that reduce the overall efficiency to the low figure of 30%. **Fig. 12.1** shows a graph that dramatically converts the potential energy contained in the cocked spring to the kinetic energy in the flying pellet. This rather complex looking diagram is perhaps the most important graph relating to spring guns in the book, since from it can be determined the distribution of energy in the system at any instant during the period of time from the trigger being pulled to the piston finally coming to rest at the end of the cylinder.

Each curve is labelled to show the particular element of the gun it represents, the thick black line running along the top being the total amount of useful energy in the system at any one moment. The vertical axis shows the energy in percentage (%) of the total input from the spring. The horizontal axis represents the time in milli-seconds (thousandths of a second) from the instant the piston starts moving.

The Spring

The spring is undoubtedly the most efficient part of an air gun since it returns practically all the energy it accumulated during the cocking stroke.

From the moment the trigger is pulled, the spring delivers its full complement of stored energy to the piston, it manages to do this very uniformly, thus its energy decrease is represented by the almost straight line from the top of the graph, at which point the spring contained 100% of the total energy, to the lowest point where it contained next to nothing. At this point the piston has compressed the air to peak pressure.

However, when the piston rebounds, the spring is again compressed by the expanding air, and this amount of energy is wasted. The problems associated with avoiding this energy loss have already been described in the chapter on pistons.

The small losses of energy incurred by the spring are associated with the friction between its coils and the inside of the piston, its ends also rub against the end of the piston and the cylinder end plug. However, in a correctly lubricated gun these losses are negligible.

Typical Energy Conversion Curves

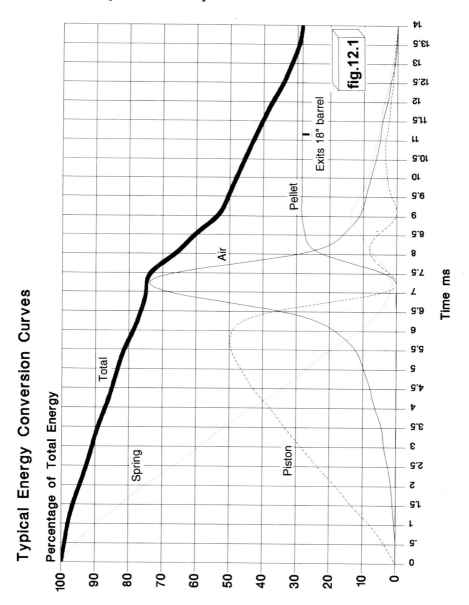

fig.12.1

Time ms

Percentage of Total Energy

Total

Spring

Air

Pellet

Piston

Exits 18" barrel

The Piston

In the chapter on pistons we mentioned that in order to produce a leak-free seal between the piston and the cylinder wall, a piston must produce some friction. It is this friction and therefore, loss of energy, that is the main cause of the Total Energy line falling during the first seven milli-seconds of the piston's forward stroke, during which time about three foot pounds of energy is lost. The frictional part of this loss can, of course, be minimised by the use of a suitable lubricant.

Turning to the line that represents the energy contained by the piston, it can be seen that the piston gains its energy from the spring at a uniform rate during the first six milli-seconds of its travel. Glancing at "Air" below it, the piston is clearly passing on this energy to the air at a uniform rate. But once the six milli-second mark is passed, the piston decelerates rapidly. The rapid slowing down of the piston is caused by the equally rapid build up of air pressure in front of it. This type of compression is called adiabatic and has already been discussed earlier in the chapter on the air. In that chapter it was pointed out that an adiabatic compression takes place without loss of heat. Now we all understand that if a gas is heated it expands, and that if it is heated within a closed container, the pressure will rise since it now cannot expand. In our case we are in a way doing two things at once, first of all we are raising the pressure of the air by compression, and secondly we are raising the pressure further by heating it by this same compression. So, both these factors added together, cause the piston to decelerate rapidly, resulting in the downward plunge of the line on the graph. At the same time, the air in the cylinder has undergone an exponential rise in energy, indicated by the sudden upward swing of the "Air" line.

The Air

The energetics of the air in a spring gun is, without doubt, an extremely difficult and complex subject to study, one must first of all start out with a knowledge of the theory of gasses. Air is considered to be made up of millions of tiny molecules, all moving about and colliding with each other within the confined space of the vessel that contains them, in our case, the cylinder. When the air is compressed, this same number of molecules are pressed into a smaller space, hence the number of collisions between the molecules is increased as also are the number of collisions between molecules and the cylinder walls. When the air is compressed by the piston, work is done on the molecules, and their velocities are increased, hence their bulk kinetic energy is raised, this addition of energy appears as a rise in temperature. Now as already stated, the compression is adiabatic and no heat energy is lost, therefore, the heat used in raising the temperature of the air during the compression stroke again becomes available to do work during the expansion of the air as it propels the pellet.

However, due to certain molecular phenomena, there are attractions between molecules that require energy to overcome them and hence a certain amount is lost in breaking these attractive forces. This loss of energy is attributed to the "non-ideality" of the air as a gas, a theoretically "ideal" gas has no internal energy losses. Unfortunately, no such gas exists.

Each individual gas is built up of different molecules, each having their own internal "non-idealities", so we experimented with alternative gasses to see if we could find one that was more efficient than air. In each case we sucked a charge of the gas into the cylinder as the gun was cocked, thereby ensuring a completely filled cylinder at atmospheric pressure for each shot.

	Air	CO_2	Argon	Butane	Freon 22	Nitrogen	Town Gas
	432	319	412	142	227	429	330
	424	304	415	57	193	420	348
	430	312	415	107	186	432	353
	420	324	422	112	153	434	345
	437	308	424	100	170	431	343
	433	324	413	106	169	432	345
	439	307	420	66	185	437	346
	439	313	418	101	148	441	350
	425	320	432	56	192	433	352
	431	318	418	103	166	438	352
Ave:	431	315	419	95	175	433	346

The figures at the at the bottom of each column are the average velocity in feet per second for that column.

It can be seen from these figures that air and nitrogen are the most efficient gases to use in air guns of conventional design, it is fortunate, therefore, that air is the gas recommended by air rifle manufacturers !! Also, of course, air is two thirds nitrogen in content.

Chapter 12 - Efficiency

Obviously the mechanical efficiency of a spring rifle can only be accurately calculated when the gun is working in either the *blowpipe* or *popgun* phase. In any other phase chemical energy enters into the system and the quantity of this energy is next to impossible to define. The total output energy is easily calculated just as long as the weight and velocity of the pellet are known. The input energy however, in both the *combustion* and *detonation* phases is made up of the energy released by the spring together with the energy released by combustion of the lubricant which in most instances will be greater than that provided by the spring.

To our way of thinking the whole system of a spring gun is beautifully subtle in its operation. Since it is a system that has evolved rather than invented, one wonders if anyone could possibly sit down and design such an unlikely scheme with any confidence of success, yet its achievements cannot be denied since there are far more spring guns manufactured world wide than any other type of airgun.

The subject of increasing the efficiency of the rifle is discussed in the next chapter called "tuning". This is the art of getting the best out of the rifle without recourse to extensive modifications.

Chapter 13
TUNING SPRING GUNS

The successful management of a spring air rifle is part science, part art, but mostly art. The science part is all wrapped up in the initial design of the gun which is not always easy to change. Up to this chapter the emphasis has been on the science content of the subject, so now it is time for the art.

The first question that must be asked is "What is meant by tuning ?" There is no simple answer to this question, each enthusiast has his own ideas on the subject; but we would suggest: *The adjustment of the rifle's characteristics and components to give the performance the owner requires.* Some owners want their guns to give the maximum power, no matter at what cost in reduced accuracy and increased recoil. Others may want maximum accuracy at whatever reduction in power; or perhaps something in between the two extremes; but it must always be remembered that there can seldom be a gain in one direction without paying a price in another. How this, or any other compromise is achieved is a matter of experience, that, like art, can't be learned from a textbook. Against these improvements the argument may be put up, *"If it ain't broken why fix it ?"* That question must be countered by the suggestion, that - *a little investigation may make it work a whole lot better.* This statement is the foundation for the many hours of tuning put into new rifles by owners who make few major alterations to the basic structure, yet manage to improve each component so that eventually the gun is as smooth as silk, going through its sequence of cocking, loading and firing without effort or resistance and with minimum noise and recoil.

The factors by which success in tuning are judged could be defined as smooth power, accuracy, consistency and continuance. Although we appear to have listed four totally separate and independent subjects, they are in fact all inextricably linked together when measuring the success of the rifle as a reliable shooting machine. Perhaps continuance is the chief factor, it sums up the other three. It is most frustrating to own a rifle which satisfies the first three immediately after tuning, then reverts back to its old inconsistent ways within a few months. An unsuitable lubricant is the usual culprit in this situation.

Tuning is normally only applied to mass produced rifles. This is because the manufacturers of such guns must satisfy a wide market for their products, therefore their guns are a compromise between a marketable product and cost.

Some operations, such as radiusing and polishing the entry to the barrel and the transfer port may have had to be foregone in the interests of economics. Also, the stock will have had to be made to fit a wide range of owners and in so doing it may be found uncomfortable by a keen enthusiast who welcomes the other characteristics of that particular rifle. In this instance he may be faced with some careful carving before the stock suits his build.

Obviously no quantity manufacturer can afford to spend extra time on each individual gun beyond testing it for velocity and accuracy. In this country the manufacturer is also very concerned that none of his products leave the factory operating at powers above the legal limit, this induces him to produce guns that tend to operate below their maximum potential.

Many air gunners, especially those involved in vermin eradication, want as much power as possible from their rifles, they need the ability to take shots at longer ranges without the necessity for the pin point accuracy of the competitive marksman. In terms of gun technology this quest for higher power is very reasonable, after all without the search for new systems, followed by their development we would still be using bows and arrows, and the wheel would not yet have been invented. This pursuit of power has its limitations; as we see it the airgun is to the firearm what the pedal cycle is to the motorcycle. The power of an airgun, especially a pump up pneumatic, is limited by the amount of energy the owner is willing to put into it. The firearm owner, on the other hand, is only limited by the ammunition's chemical energy. This is not to deny that pneumatic airguns may one day rival the smaller firearms, they probably will, but spring guns will always be on a level with pedal-cycles, relying for their power on the energy in the spring, boosted in some instances by the combustion of oil.

In each of the previous chapters the part played by individual components such as the spring, piston head or lubrication has been described; also the effects that the various differing designs of these components are likely to have on the operation of the rifle. Taking all these variable factors together offers more opportunities for dissimilar combinations than a football coupon. Also, and this is most important, altering one component slightly may upset the others completely, perhaps resulting in a totally unstable rifle; that is a rifle whose velocity goes up and down like a yo-yo. Likely culprits for producing instability are the lubricant or piston head, if there is too much unsuitable lubricant present in front of the head instability will result.

Chapter 13 - Tuning Spring Guns

Tuning a spring gun is somewhat similar to weather forecasting, each climatic factor may foretell a fine day, but an unexpected variation in temperature however slight many miles away, may upset the wind direction, this in turn upsets the whole pattern over the area in question, and it rains. Here we have a classic example of chaos. The study of chaos is a somewhat new science which requires enormous computing capacity to analyze an almost limitless number of variables. A small variation in any one factor, particularly in a spring gun, may substantially influence the final outcome; hence the comparison with a football coupon.

Probably the foundation to any tuning operation is experience, experience not only of airguns in general but also a deep knowledge and understanding of the gun in question, each one is different. One must know the model's strengths and weaknesses too. One must be prepared to take notes of any alterations, and the reasons for making them. Obviously a chrono is an essential piece of equipment, for without one, one is working in the dark. Always be prepared to fit a less powerful spring; this is never an easy course to consider, especially when an increase in velocity is the goal, but it is very often the secret of success.

Just to emphasise this statement the following figures were obtained during an experiment to demonstrate that there is in fact an optimum value for the input energy in any particular rifle.

Input Energy. Ft. lbs.	Output Ft. lbs. 14 Grain Pellet.	Output Ft. lbs. 12 Grain Pellet.
38.65	5.85 *(15.2%)*	5.25 *(13.6%)*
36.79	6.13 *(16.6%)*	4.84 *(13.0%)*
33.03	6.24 *(18.9%)*	5.50 *(16.6%)*
24.74	6.75 *(27.3%)*	5.84 *(23.6%)*
20.91	6.58 *(31.5%)*	5.44 *(26.0%)*
18.17	5.72 *(31.5%)*	5.50 *(30.3%)*
14.17	3.47 *(24.5%)*	4.33 *(30.5%)*

(The figures in brackets are percentage efficiency)

The same spring was used throughout, but coils were cut from it as the experiment progressed. The correct velocity at each power setting was determined by the firing of at least five shots.

Never be disappointed by failure because it is usually the gateway to success. Failure tells you positively that you have gone the wrong way, or perhaps gone too far in the right direction. For instance, the size of the transfer port often seems too small and there is the temptation to enlarge it. However, suppose the larger hole only yields a small velocity increase and it is decided to risk further drilling, only to find that the velocity has now fallen. Two things now become clear; the initial diameter increase was about correct for that particular gun, but worse, the hole must now be accurately bored out even larger to accept a bush which has a correct sized hole running through it. At the same time this exercise illustrates why it is imperative to have the equipment and ability necessary to restore the gun to its original state before any major alterations are attempted, just in case things go wrong.

When embarking on tuning, or any other alteration to an air arm, it is well worth taking the extra time and effort required to keep notes and small sketches of what has been done, also the date on which the work was carried out. Such details as pellet type and weight together with velocities and perhaps copies of the target groups are worth keeping too, it all makes an invaluable reference source not only for that gun, but also for comparison with others but not necessarily of the same type.

Great perseverance is often necessary when the expected improvement does not materialise. There is always a good reason why a rifle does not perform correctly, its detection and subsequent cure may require immense patience and experience. Experience (something you learn the hard way) can only be gained by working on difficult rifles, easy problems provide little knowledge. The careful analysis of failure is probably more important than success because success is accepted and seldom investigated. In the old days of steam locomotives there was a saying amongst footplate men which went something like, *"It takes a bad engine to make a good fireman"*. Very applicable to airguns too.

It is too easy to expect too much from tuning a rifle. It is sheer folly to buy a small rifle and expect to be able to tune it up satisfactorily to the performance of a larger one; after all it is impossible to get a quart out of a pint pot. It makes far more sense to spend time investigating the capabilities of the available rifles. Then, long before any consideration is given to tuning, the model which meets your requirements in its unmodified form should be purchased. Tuning, as explained to us by an old hand in the gun trade, "Is only making it work right."

Chapter 13 - Tuning Spring Guns

Never embark on a major alteration one wet Sunday afternoon just because boredom has replaced an outing. Monday morning will bring frustration and a damaged rifle. Any alteration must be carefully planned beforehand, all the components that may be required such as a new spring, a pot of suitable grease, engineer's tools and above all a chrono must all be to hand before the job is started. The rifle cost you a lot of money, so it is well worth planning the operation carefully, just as though it was surgery; in some instances you will have only one chance, so you must be confident that you have the ability, tools and experience to get it right first go. Undoubtedly the whole undertaking will take many hours longer than you ever anticipated, so don't be disappointed if the job is not complete next day.

In the chapters about the cylinder and piston head, we described the importance of the surface finish of the cylinder bore, we showed how the slight grooves and scratches left by the honing stones serve to store the lubricant. Any machining operation leaves a surface which, highly magnified, resembles corrugated paper; obviously two sheets of this paper will not move across one another easily if the ridges on one sheet interlock with the furrows on the other. If the ridges move at right angles to the furrows a compromise situation exists which can only be excelled by the ideal arrangement where ridges and furrows move in the same direction. This configuration must be encouraged in any acceptable gun, otherwise it will not have that smooth action which is the hall mark of a carefully made machine.

It is an odd fact of life that the machining operations normally and correctly used during the manufacture of an air rifle very often leave the finish on each surface in the worst possible state to work smoothly with its partner. For instance both the cylinder and its piston are both shaped by rotation, rotation either of the component itself or the tool that shaped it. This leaves a series of microscopic grooves running around the two surfaces which in service will be expected to slide across each other. Similarly, parts of the trigger mechanism which must slide effortlessly over each other are often manufactured by processes which generate scratches across their surfaces.

In the case of a cylinder in which a plastic piston head will move, the scratches serve a useful purpose, and it is better not to polish them away. So it now becomes imperative that the machining marks on the piston, especially those on the tail, be removed with fine emery paper rubbed along the contact surfaces, otherwise the gun will feel very rough during the cocking stroke. A final polish on a buffing wheel, again running along the piston, will guarantee a silk smooth movement.

The surfaces of trigger mechanisms are best left alone unless the owner is used to working accurately with the finest carborundum or arkansas stones. Too much enthusiasm here will result in a dangerous rifle or the very costly replacement of a complete trigger unit. Nevertheless, the final goal is always to ensure that the rubbing surfaces are highly polished and that the final strokes of the polishing medium all run in the direction of movement.

The polish on any metal surface is really only a matter of degree, however good it looks; a powerful magnifying glass will always show up imperfections. Improvements can be made by a bit more hard work, but greater magnification will show perfection has not yet been achieved. Remember that the smoothness of the surface is best judged by drawing a finger nail across it rather than the soft end of a finger; the nail is remarkably sensitive and can detect the slightest imperfections with ease.

While on the subject of surface finish probably the most difficult to examine is the inside of the cylinder. But if a piece of a hand mirror, or even a discarded dental mirror, is dropped down the tube the light reflected from it will illuminate the surface making the quality of its surface very clear.

Obviously any attempt at tuning must be preceded by checking the existing velocity with a chrono, especially when a power alteration is the objective. Once the operation is complete, further chrono readings must be taken using the same brand of pellets as before, checking for a change in power, hopefully in the right direction. Suppose that a different piston head, or spring, has been fitted, or perhaps an alteration to the shape of the transfer port has been made in the hope of achieving a higher velocity; with luck the second chrono reading will be much higher than the first and victory may be claimed.

Unfortunately this apparent success may not be altogether true, there is a pitfall here ready to trap the unwary. During the alterations to the rifle it has of course been necessary to strip it completely while at the same time all the old oil and grease will have been cleaned out. Once the job is complete, new grease, probably the same brand as the old, is used to re-lubricate the rifle, this then is the basis of the trap. It is probable that it is the fresh charge of grease which is fully or partially responsible for the velocity increase, the active ingredients of the original charge having already been burned away.

Chapter 13 - Tuning Spring Guns

The difficulty of making any alteration to a spring gun's performance without upsetting what we have called the "Grease Pattern" has always been a major obstacle, it can have a profound effect on the results. During many of our experiments we had to go to endless lengths to avoid removing the piston and thereby upsetting the grease pattern, because in so doing the results of the experiment would, in most instances, be rendered meaningless. In any experiment it is of vital importance to change only one factor at a time; when this factor is not the lubrication one has to go to incredible lengths to avoid disturbing the existing grease pattern because it is a major factor in the gun's performance.

Many times during our experiments we needed to know whether air was leaking past the piston, or perhaps from the breech joint. We needed a quick and reliable method of blocking the barrel at the breech so that the question of leakage could be swiftly answered. In these situations we again made use of the *Sputnik* which we described in chapter 6. When in position the sputnik allows the action of the gun to be seen in a sort of slow-motion; the piston rushes forward then slows to a crawl as the air escapes. At the same time it is possible to determine the point of leakage, if it is passing the piston it is easily heard while if it is escaping at the breech it is possible to locate the leak by the use of spray on shaving cream.

There is a point here worth mentioning about breech seals, when dealing with the early leather type it is imperative that they be kept moist with oil, if not they dry up, shrink and will leak. A well oiled leather seal can be as good as a modern 'O' ring any day.

Another area in which "time" is important in airgunning is in what is called "Lock-Time". This is the very short interval of time between the trigger being pulled and the pellet leaving the muzzle. We airgunners have incorrectly borrowed the term from the world of firearms where it is used to define the time between the pulling of the trigger and the hammer striking the primer in the base of the cartridge, an even smaller interval of time than ours. Obviously a short lock time in an air gun is an advantage since it reduces the likelihood of the pellet being influenced by vibrations building up in the gun once the trigger has been released.

Lock time is measured in milliseconds, that is thousandths of a second. Its duration obviously depends on many factors, barrel length being very important. In general terms, a pneumatic has a shorter lock time than a gas ram which has a shorter time than a spring, while a pneumatic pistol has the shortest time of all. Typical values would be 8.6ms for a pneumatic rifle, 10.5ms for a gas ram and 13ms for spring, while the pistol is in the order of only 3.8ms milliseconds.

The equipment necessary for measuring lock time is shown in **fig 13.1**. The chrono starts counting simultaneously as the trigger releases as the magnet attached to it closes a reed switch, the chrono is then stopped as the pellet shatters the pencil lead placed across the muzzle. In the photograph the muzzle has been deliberately drawn back from the pencil lead to make it visible.

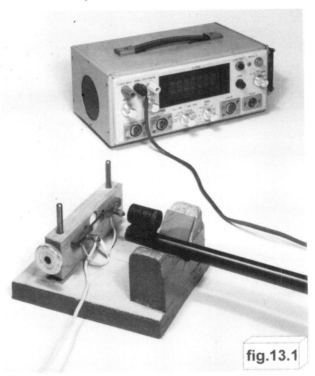

fig.13.1

There is not much that the owner of an air arm can do to reduce its lock time, certainly a stiffer spring might reduce the time whilst simultaneously increasing the velocity, but the adverse effects of a more powerful spring would probably outweigh the anticipated benefits of the reduced lock time through increased recoil and vibration. Obviously an increase in velocity in any type of arm must imply a reduction in lock time.

The process of tuning may be extended far beyond simple finishing and polishing into the realms of "customisation." In this field far reaching and major modifications to the standard rifle may be considered, for instance the barrel may be cut short, or a completely new set of internal parts made and fitted. In all probability the original stock will be replaced by one of walnut designed to fit the figure and fancy of the owner. This is a very specialised subject and highly skilled firms such as *Venom Arms of Halesowen* have developed it to the point where one of their rifles can take its place beside classic Best English shotguns.

It is worth remembering that when Mr. Wesley, in his book "Air-Guns and Air-Pistols" mentions that various rifles or pistols were very powerful, he was speaking about them in comparison with other arms on the market at that time and not in terms of their actual velocity. He was certainly not comparing them with the capability of those available today. It is better therefore, not to try to bring these "old timers" up to the standards of today, they are a far too valuable piece of history to be ruined in the imagined hope of super power, there really is no crock of gold at the rainbow's end.

Whatever the results obtained by tuning spring guns, either disappointing or successful, they will always remain a challenge and a source of fascination. They are an enigmatic machine - a maze to which there is neither beginning nor end.

Chapter 13 - Tuning Spring Guns

Chapter 14
PNEUMATICS

Although the spring gun has arguably been around for longer than the pneumatic, the spring system only returned to favour towards the end of the last century as a viable gun, and even then only capable of shooting darts or pellets at very low velocities. In all probability the very early technology of metalworking was not high enough to produce the parts to a satisfactory standard, also the making of a successful spring must have been next to impossible.

The building of a viable pneumatic, on the other hand was not quite so difficult. Although they were far more complicated and costly than the firearms of the day they had one great advantage, they could be used in bad weather. The powder in the pan of a flint lock cannot be ignited if the wind blows the sparks or the rain wets the powder.

In most instances the design of early pneumatics was based on the concept of a removable reservoir which could be charged by pumping with a separate pump. The reservoir was either the butt itself or a globe, usually screwed beneath the lock of the gun. These fascinating old guns, whose calibre was in the region of half an inch, have been the subject of many in-depth studies, so we will not spend time adding to the list, except to say that they were a practical gun and could produce powers equal to the black powder arms of the day. It is important to realise however, that they worked at pressures of about 600 PSI, this is very low when compared with modern rifles operating at about 3,000 PSI. Also, they were always built as multi shot arms, that is they could fire more than one shot after each pumping; inevitably the velocity of the shots fell as the pressure in the reservoir reduced but in skilled hands this was a surmountable difficulty. It has long been our contention that if the early airgun makers had had an equivalent of our modern 'O' ring, airguns would have played a much larger part in the making of world history. Leakage at the valve and joints was always a barrier to the popularity and further development of this type of arm.

Early attempts to manufacture guns with their own built in pumps were never really successful because the pump was always a simple piston and rod system - like a bicycle pump. High pressures could never be achieved with this arrangement within a reasonable number of pump strokes and the idea lay dormant until Sheridan in America built rifles with a toggle lever system operating the piston. Guns functioning on this design, commonly known as "pump-ups," were very popular and several firms in America and Japan still make them. We will go into the technicalities of this design in the following chapter; but their popularity has diminished since the development of pre-charged rifles because of the effort that must be put into them before they are ready to shoot. Also, in most instances they are only capable of firing one shot from each air charge; some will fire two or more, but of widely differing velocities.

A variation of the pump-up system is known as the "single-stroke pneumatic". As its name implies the single-stroke is charged by only one stroke of the pump handle. In this design the pump piston is normally driven forward by a pair of toggle links, but there is no reservoir as such in which the compressed air may be stored. Instead the air is held at high pressure between the piston and the exhaust valve from where it is released when the trigger is pulled, opening the exhaust valve.

The single-stroke system is usually to be found in rifles and pistols designed for competitive target shooting where accuracy and consistency are the chief requirements. Attempts have been made to use the system for high power sporting rifles, however in our opinion the results have had limited appeal because of the difficulty of completing the lever's stroke when the pressure in front of the piston is at its greatest.

Pre-charged rifles have attained immense popularity during the last decade, they have developed hand in hand with an increased interest in diving. Diving clubs, shops and companies have been set up in most large towns, each having facilities for supplying high pressure air at a reasonable cost. The airgun enthusiast can now have his cylinder filled with enough air to last him months at a remarkably low price. All he then has to do is couple his rifle to the cylinder with a suitable tube to replenish its charge after shooting. Obviously great care must be exercised when handling air at 3,000 PSI; cylinders, tubes and couplings must be in very good condition, as also the gun itself. One word of severe warning, **never** under any circumstances attempt to fill an airgun with oxygen. Oxygen forms a highly explosive mixture when it comes in contact with oil, inevitably there will be oil present somewhere in the gun and the result will be a disaster not only for the gun but also for anyone near it.

In 1872 Giffard took out a patent for a pre-charged cartridge which could be filled either with air or carbon dioxide. Each cartridge was fitted with its own individual bullet ready for loading into the rifle. However, it seems that none were made on a commercial basis and the idea lapsed, probably because of the difficulty of manufacturing them accurately enough for total interchangeability. Also, reliable sealing was probably very difficult to achieve.

The idea of individually pre-charged cartridges became a reality a few years ago and several models have had varying degrees of commercial success. These can be charged singly by fitting them onto a hand operated pump, or in multiples of six at a time from a diver's cylinder by the use of a special adapter. The piston of the hand operated pump is again driven by a toggle system similar to that used on pump-ups and is capable of delivering pressures in the order of 3,000 PSI. The concept of individual cartridges lends itself to many applications such as revolvers or bolt action magazine fed rifles, but in technical terms they are the same as any other single shot pneumatic rifle.

The normal layout for a pneumatic is for the air cylinder, or pump cylinder to be placed beneath the barrel. This is the most logical position because the trigger mechanism and release valve can then be placed at the butt end of the tube while the filling valve, or pump, can be built into the front end, beneath the muzzle. The air from the release valve is then guided upwards through a short transfer port directly into the barrel behind the pellet.

A pneumatic rifle could be said to work best in the *blowpipe* phase, a term normally used only when speaking about spring guns, but it describes the action of a pneumatic very nicely too. The pellet should be waiting at the start of the rifling for the air blast to send it up the bore, the air itself should not have to waste energy in overcoming anything but the slightest pellet tightness before it leaves the breech. Any initial pellet tightness at the start of its journey will inevitably result in poor consistency since no two pellets offer exactly the same resistance to the rifling.

The use of a bolt to seal the breech once the pellet has been inserted into the barrel offers the facility of pushing the pellet forward past the transfer port and into the rifling, it is for this very important reason that bolts always have either a pin or a hollow sleeve at their front so that each pellet is seated correctly into the bore. Closing the bolt forces the pellet into the rifling so that the energy required to engrave the rifling on the pellet comes from the owner and not the air. The energy required to form a pellet to fit the barrel may be considerable especially if the pellet's walls are of a thick heavy section. Since the pneumatic system operates more efficiently when firing heavier pellets, the use of a bolt to position the pellet correctly is almost mandatory in this type of arm.

Lubrication of a pre-charged pneumatic is best carried out after carefully reading the makers instructions, we say this because the wrong type of lubricant will probably rot the valve seals or 'O' rings. In any case only a very thin oil is necessary except in the case of pump-ups where the pivots of the lever system come under considerable strain, especially when they are used as body building machines. Each pivot needs a plentiful supply of lubricant, we like to use grease. At the same time the crosshead which connects the link to the piston requires lubrication otherwise it will score the walls of the pump tube.

Repeating what we have already said in the earlier chapter about barrels. In the case of a pneumatic, to obtain the greatest accuracy the lubrication must be supplied by a film of lubricant on the pellet itself because little, if any, oil will be supplied by the air.

Chapter 15
CHARGING PNEUMATICS

Before we get too involved in the very important subject of controlling the air used to drive the pellets along the barrels of our pneumatics, we must first look at how the air first becomes compressed. Also the amount of potential energy that it stores when compressed, and at the same time the amount of energy expended in compressing it.

Working accurately with compressed air without a pressure gauge would be like working on any airgun without a chronograph, it would be very difficult indeed, mostly imagination. These days we speak with confidence of air pressures and with as much accuracy as telling the time to the nearest minute, but it was not always so. It was only in 1850 that the pressure gauge, as we know it, was invented by a Frenchman called Eugene Bourdon. The instrument he made must have immediately removed much of the doubt and danger from the manufacture of airguns and injected an element of safety not only into the world of airguns, but also into any machinery driven by steam such as ships, factories and locomotives.

fig.15.1

The gauges we see today (**fig 15.1**) are exactly the same as the one he made, the only difference being one of style and presentation, the principle itself has not changed. Any oval shaped tube closed at one end and formed into a semicircle tends to straighten itself out as the pressure inside it increases. Of course before 1850 it had been possible to measure pressure by means of a what is called a dead weight gauge, but these were slow and cumbersome to use. They relied on the air pressure below a piston, of known cross sectional area, pushing it upwards within a close fitting cylinder and just balancing the weights placed on top of it.

In modern times a similar procedure to a dead weight gauge may be used to determine the pressure within a globe or butt reservoir while charging them with their own rod and piston pump; assuming that is that no normal gauge is available. If the pump rod is placed on the bathroom scales while pumping, the scales will indicate the force on the rod. It is not difficult to measure the diameter of the piston and from that to calculate its cross sectional area. If the force on the rod in pounds is divided by the area of the piston in square inches, the result will be the pressure in pounds per square inch in front of the piston.

Little was known about metal fatigue in those early days and several instances are recorded where globe reservoirs exploded as they were being pumped. The sudden release of such a large volume of air had disastrous results not only on the man operating the pump, but also on the bystanders. From this it must be understood that high pressure air is very dangerous because once released it expands instantaneously. It is for this reason that reservoirs are filled with oil or water when they are being tested, neither of which can be compressed, so contain no energy. If an oil filled reservoir should split while under pressure no great harm will be done, other than a nasty mess.

Until recently air pressure was always spoken of in terms of Pounds per Square Inch (PSI) but these days the term Bar has become very common. One bar is the amount of pressure normally exerted by the atmosphere on each square inch of the earth's surface, but since this pressure varies with the weather and atmospheric conditions the unit has been internationally agreed as being 14.22 PSI.

The energy stored by a compressed air may be calculated as long as its volume and pressure are known.

The equation is:

$$E = \frac{P_1 \, V_1 \, \mathrm{Log}_e \, (V_2/V_1)}{12} \quad \text{Ft. lbs.}$$

$P_1 =$ Initial pressure. In our case this is always atmospheric at 14.4 PSI.
$V_1 =$ Initial Volume. That is the volume of free air pumped into the reservoir.
$V_2 =$ Final Volume. In our case the volume of the reservoir.

Log_e. These are natural logarithms or logs to the base e.

In the above equation the only quantity that is not easy to establish by measurement is the Initial Volume V_1, but more about this later, all the remainder, such as the final volume or the final pressure, may be established by direct measurement.

However we may again use the simple equation that we used earlier in Chapter 7 to establish this initial volume. That is:

$$P_1 \, V_1 = P_2 \, V_2$$

From this we have:

$$V_1 = \frac{P_2 \, V_2}{P_1}$$

Suppose we have a reservoir whose volume is 0.17 cubic inches at a pressure of 1,300 PSI. The first thing we must establish is the volume of free air that is pumped into it, V_1. From the above equation we may determine this by multiplying the final pressure by its volume and dividing by the initial atmospheric pressure of 14.4 PSI. This calculation will give us **15.35 Cu.ins**.

By using the first equation it is possible to calculate the energy contained by the compressed air within the reservoir. This will give a stored energy figure of **83 Ft.lbs.** But the actual amount of energy required to charge the reservoir is considerably greater, depending on the speed at which the reservoir is filled.

If it is filled quickly then more energy will be expended and it will become hotter than if it is filled slowly.

An easy way to demonstrate this fact is by the use of a pump up rifle. If it is loaded and cocked, then pumped up fast and fired immediately, its velocity will be slightly higher than when it is pumped slowly, or left to cool before it is fired. The reason for this is that when it is pumped fast there is less time during which the heat may escape, in other words the pumping is done nearly adiabatically. The heat in the air causes its pressure to be higher through expansion, so when the gun is fired there is more energy available to drive the pellet. If, on the other hand, the gun is allowed to cool before it is fired, the heat energy will have left the air and its pressure will be lower, therefore the velocity will also be reduced.

This heating and cooling of the air can easily and dramatically be demonstrated with a broad rubber band. If it is suddenly stretched while in contact with the forehead its warming will be very clearly felt; then as it is returned suddenly to its original length it will become surprisingly cool. If on the other hand the band is stretched slowly no rise in temperature will be felt, neither will it feel cool if it is released again slowly. This lack of detection of the temperature change is caused by the slowness of the action, allowing the temperature change to occur unperceived.

This simple comparison between the stretching of a rubber band and the filling of an air reservoir is a very helpful way of forming a clear idea of the characteristics of compressed air, it demonstrates that only part of the total pumping energy will be used to propel the pellet up the barrel. This of course brings us to the two important words which crop up all the time when talking about compressing or releasing air, they are of course Isothermal and Adiabatic. Isothermal comes from the Greek Isos "Equal" and Thermos "Heat". So when the reservoir is pumped up or emptied slowly, or the rubber band stretched and relaxed slowly its temperature remains about the same, an Isothermic action.

Alternatively the word Adiabatic stems from the Greek Adiabatos "Not-passed-through", in other words the heat is not passed through the walls of the compression cylinder and therefore remains within the air, which of course it does if the compression is very sudden. This change in temperature is very clear in the case of the suddenly stretched and relaxed rubber band, the heating and cooling are easily detected as it is held against the skin.

As we said earlier, it is not always easy to establish the volume of the high pressure air in a small reservoir such as an air cartridge. Measuring the various diameters and lengths of each component, then calculating the volume is seldom satisfactory on account of the chamfer or radius at each corner. We found the best answer to the problem lies in weighing the complete reservoir before stripping and reassembling it under water, making sure that no air bubbles are included. Once assembled and the water droplets removed from the outside, the reservoir should be weighed again. The weight of the water inside it may be established by subtracting the empty weight from the full weight. Water weighs exactly one gramme per cubic centimetre, from this it is easy to establish the volume inside the cartridge.

Normally in airgunning we use the old Imperial units such as feet, inches, square inches or pounds, but when establishing volumes it is usually easier to use the modern metric system because the smaller units are more commonly accessible. If scales only calibrated in grains are available, the weights may be converted by reference to the data at the end of this book.

On many occasions we wanted to be able to cross check our calculations by measuring the actual amount of air exhausted from the barrel of a pneumatic. The equipment we made for this purpose is shown in **fig 15.2**. It has an oil soaked cup shaped leather piston moving as freely as possible inside a plastic tube whose diameter is about three inches. The piston can rise through about fifteen inches which gives it a total capacity of about 2,000 cm^3. If the inlet tube is made an airtight fit onto the muzzle of the gun to be tested and the gun fired, the piston will be driven upwards so that the volume below it contains the air expelled by the gun. When we first made the cylinder we calibrated it by pouring water into it from a high quality measuring cylinder, our cylinder now has a scale of Cubic Centimetres marked on its outside from which we can immediately determine the volume of air forced into it.

In the previous chapter we pointed out that it is next to impossible to achieve high air pressures with a simple rod and piston pump; to illustrate this point we will go through a simple experiment. Suppose a reservoir is to be filled to a pressure of 1,000 PSI with such a pump. First of all the bathroom scales may be used to see how much force can be exerted on the pump handle, and we find perhaps that a weight of 16$^1/_2$ stone, that is 231 Lbs., is available. Although at first sight it might appear that would be the maximum thrust we could exert on the piston rod, practical experiment shows that this can be exceeded by about 50%, that is if the person doing the pumping leans over the handle and bounces on it. Not an easy exercise, it also demands a robust pump capable of withstanding the treatment. So we have a maximum force of 346 pounds available with which to push on the pump rod. A piston whose diameter is 5/8" has a frontal area of 0.307 sq.ins. If the force on the rod is divided by the area of the piston a figure of 1127 PSI will be produced.

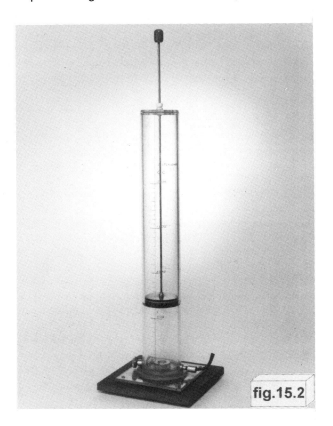

fig.15.2

From this calculation it is clear that a heavy man using a $^5/_8$" diameter pump should be able to achieve a pressure of about 1,000 PSI. But again, from practical experience we know it is not an easy task, and to fill quite a small reservoir by this method takes perseverance. Of course the first pump strokes are easy, but as the pressure builds up the task becomes progressively harder.

Early books on airguns mention that very often two men would work side by side to complete the task.

The diameter of the piston could be reduced which would make the pumping a lot easier, but the volume delivered at each stroke would also be reduced. This would mean that the number of pump strokes would have to be increased before the reservoir is filled. With this thought in mind it is worth mentioning that if the piston's diameter were to be reduced by half, its surface area would be reduced by four. So in the above situation, if a pump with a $^5/_{16}$"dia. piston had been used its frontal area would have only amounted to 0.077 sq.ins. and using the same force on the rod a pressure of 4500 PSI could theoretically be generated.

However, it must also be realised that if the pump has a stroke length of twelve inches, then in the first instance the swept volume would have been 0.307 x 12, while in the second case the volume would have been 0.077 x 12, resulting in swept volumes of 3.68 Cu.ins. or 0.92 Cu.ins. respectively. This means that four times the number of strokes would have to be applied to the smaller pump to force the same volume into the reservoir. This is a calculated and theoretical figure, in practice five times the number of strokes would be a more probable figure.

Certain practical difficulties become magnified when the diameter of the pump becomes very small and the pressures high, probably the design of the valves is the greatest. Obviously the amount of lost volume must be kept to an absolute minimum under these circumstances, otherwise the compressed air will fill the lost volume at the end of the stroke and none will be forced out through the exhaust valve and into the reservoir. Ideally the piston should completely fill all the airspace available at the front of the cylinder pushing all the air that was in front of it out into the reservoir, but this is not possible in practice. Another practical difficulty hindering the construction of a simple high pressure pump is the strength of the piston rod which inevitably must be long and slim. It is therefore liable to bend when the pressure in front of the piston rises to its maximum value.

Many of the difficulties associated with the construction of rod and piston pumps may be overcome by making them into what is called *Multi-stage pumps*. In this system two or more pistons and cylinders are used, each one smaller than the last. The first stage will have a large bore with a long stroke whose out going air is passed into a much smaller cylinder, perhaps of only one tenth or less of the volume of its predecessor. This may then pass its output to an even smaller cylinder. In this manner very high pressures may be attained with comparative ease, though the construction of the pump does not lend itself to incorporation into the gun itself. Such compressors are usually machines on their own driven by an electric motor. Years ago, before diving shops and clubs became established, we built such a machine ourselves. It had four stages of compression and lived in a tank of lubricating oil, when in top condition it was capable of producing the prodigious pressure of 10,000 PSI; these days the local diving shop supplies the air with much less hassle.

Toggle Lever

Probably the most successful pump which can be built directly into a rifle or pistol is the one based on the toggle lever system. This design lends itself ideally to the requirement of compressing air by a simple piston and rod pump. The operating handle causes the levers to advance the piston fast at the beginning of its stroke where the resistance of the air being compressed is low. As the piston approaches the end of the cylinder and the pressure of the air increases, the thrust of the piston also rises because of the altered geometry of the levers. At the end of the piston's stroke, when the air pressure in front of it is at its greatest, the thrust generated by the levers is also enormous. Pressures in excess of 3,000 PSI may be obtained with this system.

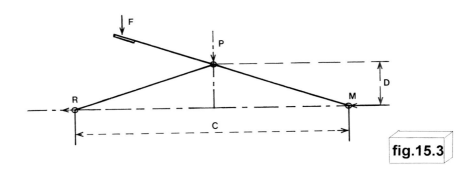

fig.15.3

Fig 15.3 shows the toggle lever system in diagrammatic form. In an airgun application one of the links is always extended to form a handle. This extension again increases the leverage of the system, and in most instances the lever extends beyond point **P** to perhaps three times the length of the link, thus tripling the force on the pivot **P** when pressure is applied to the handle at **F**. The pressure on the handle **F** forces the pivot **P** downwards reducing dimension **D** and in so doing pushing the point **R**, which in our case is the end of the piston rod, towards the reservoir. Point **R** must move forward because point **M** is held firmly by a pin at the muzzle. Although the diagram shows the two links to be of equal length, very often in practice one is usually slightly longer than the other. The difference has a negligible effect on the final result.

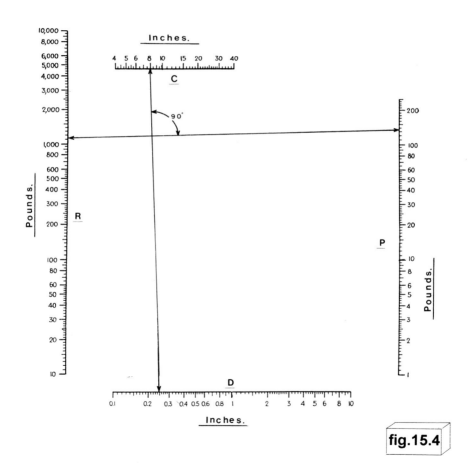

fig.15.4

Fig 15.4 is a chart which may be used to determine the thrust generated on the piston by a toggle lever system. To use this chart two lines should be drawn on a piece of tracing paper which are exactly at right angles to each other. The paper may then be moved about the chart lining up with the three known quantities, the unknown quantity will then be indicated by the remaining line. In the example shown a force of 45 Lbs. is applied to the end of the lever and the distance between the end of the lever at point **F** is three times the distance from **P** to **M**. The pressure on the point **P** is therefore three times 45 Lbs. One horizontal line on the movable paper may now be set to coincide with 135 Lbs. on the scale marked **P**. Measurements taken from the gun with an engineer's rule show that when the dimension **C** is 8" the dimension **D** is 0.25". It is now possible to position the vertical line on the movable paper so that it coincides with both these measurements on the scales **C** and **D**. Once this has been done the fourth line will be seen to coincide with a pressure of 1,150 Pounds on the scale **R**.

The above chart is based on the equation:

$$\frac{R}{P} = \frac{C}{4D}$$

Obviously a thrust of 1,150 Lbs. is a very large figure when compared with the original 45 Lbs. applied to the handle. In our example there was still a further quarter of an inch (Dimension **D**) to go before the links **R,P,M** are forced into a straight line, where they would generate the maximum thrust. However, in this situation the piston is usually already at the end of its stroke because normally the system is adjusted so that the maximum length of dimension **C** is slightly less than the combined lengths **R P M** when the piston is hard up against the end of the reservoir. This results in a slight stretching of the metal parts at the moment the point **P** passes through the straight line position. This slight strain has the advantage of holding the pump handle close up to the remainder of the rifle even when there is no air in front of the piston to retain it after the rifle has been fired.

From the above it would appear that since the piston was being pressed hard against the reservoir end with a thrust in excess of 1,150 Lbs. then the maximum air pressure in front of it must have been at least that figure divided by the frontal area of the piston. This is not necessarily so because in any pneumatic system there are always small amounts of "lost volume" which will lower the final pressure, and at high pressures even a small amount of lost volume will have a marked effect on the final figure. In a pump up pneumatic there must be a transfer port between the pump piston and the inlet valve to the reservoir, this will lower the final pressure, even when its diameter is very small. There are still other volumes to be considered, the inlet valve itself as well the clearance around the piston in front of the seal all add up to a reduction in the overall efficiency of the system.

Of course the air that is trapped in the lost volumes after the final stroke of the pump is not totally wasted. When the gun is fired that air passes through into the reservoir to boost the power of the pellet. This fact may be easily demonstrated by charging the gun on two occasions with say five strokes, in the first instance the pump lever is returned to the normal closed position against the body tube, while in the second instance it is left hanging down. In this position any trapped air is released from the pockets of lost volume and the velocity of the shot will be lower than that fired with the lever closed.

For maximum consistency a pneumatic must be pumped not only with the same number of strokes but the rate of pumping must also be fairly constant so as to maintain a similar pressure and heat build up at each stroke. Also, the gun should be allowed to cool down to the ambient temperature of the day before it is fired; this will ensure that each pellet has the exact same amount of energy behind it at every shot. On one occasion we carefully measured the energy that had to be expended in pumping up one of these rifles, then checked the energy of the pellet as it left the barrel. From these figures we calculated the overall efficiency of the system and were horrified to find it to be in the order of 5%.

A question that often arises in regard to pumping up pneumatics is the imagined danger of an explosion through the ignition of the lubricating oil by the heat generated as a result of compression, as happens in a spring rifle or diesel engine. This is a next to impossible occurrence when hand pumping because the rate of compression is far too slow to generate temperatures high enough to cause the oil to burn. However, an explosion is guaranteed if anyone attempts to fill a pneumatic with pure oxygen. Oxygen forms an explosive mixture when it comes in contact with oil, and there is bound to be oil somewhere in the gun. All pressure gauges made for use on oxygen cylinders carry the direction *"Use no oil"*. That should be good enough warning for all of us !

By far the easiest way to fill the reservoir of any pneumatic is to use a diver's air bottle. These cylinders may be purchased in various sizes and all are capable of holding air at 3,000 PSI. They may be refilled remarkably cheaply any number of times, but they must be examined and tested at frequent intervals to make sure they are safe and that no corrosion has started internally, also that they have not been damaged externally. The rifle is coupled to the bottle by a flexible hose fitted with a gauge so that the pressure in the gun may be monitored and the valve on the bottle closed as soon a the required pressure is reached. Once the initial high cost of the cylinder has been accepted this simple and inexpensive system is the basis for filling most pre-charged rifles and air cartridges. Provided the equipment is kept in good order and inspected frequently it is a very safe procedure.

Having looked at the various methods by which air may be charged into the reservoir we will look now at the next stage in the sequence, that is what volume and pressure the owner is likely to need to drive the pellet at the required velocity. We carried out an extensive study some years ago using my *projector* to establish the power of the pellet when using differing volumes and pressures, also various lengths of barrel and calibres.

The Projector

Before describing the results of this investigation it is worth while spending some time describing the *projector* shown in **fig 15.5**. We built this piece of equipment so that we could study various difficult aspects of airguns. It is constructed so as to be very firm, rigid and vibrationless when fixed to the floor by a strong central bolt, the top plate which carries the barrel-fixing together with the scope has a limited lateral movement to allow for final alignment with the target. The precision spirit level rests on two mushroom shaped studs (**inset fig 15.5**) which pass through the barrel outer casing to rest on the barrel itself allowing the three adjusting screws in the base to set the barrel dead level. Barrels of any size or calibre may be fitted into the outer casing and held firmly by split nylon collars machined to suit.

The breech of the projector is cut from an HW 35 rifle and reconstructed to couple the air reservoir to the barrel; any size of barrel may be modified to fit into the breech block where it is held by two grub screws. The breech is held firmly shut by the normal HW 35 latch, but the whole reservoir swings sideways when it is open, allowing an unimpeded view through the bore for preliminary sighting by eye or bore telescope. The reservoir, which also encompasses the release valve, has a maximum capacity of 1.5 Cu.ins. and can withstand pressures in excess of 4,000 PSI. A selection of collars may be inserted inside the reservoir to reduce its capacity as dictated by the experiment in progress. The minimum practical volume being 0.12 Cu.ins.

fig.15.5

The reservoir is charged by manipulating the three small valves until the correct pressure is established. Before firing, the shut-off valve attached directly to the reservoir is closed so that none of the air in the flexible tube can take part in the shot. The trigger mechanism is shown in the cocked position; when the horizontal lever is pressed down it releases the vertical lever which swings back around the curved end of the horizontal lever. The lower end of the vertical lever holds the valve closed, but when the lever is released the whole valve spindle moves outwards under the influence of the air pressure inside the reservoir. This outward thrust is generated because the outer end of the spindle is of greater diameter than the sealing diameter. The valve, transfer port and barrel are all in alignment allowing the air an unimpeded flow behind the pellet once the valve opens.

By using the projector and various barrels, including those coupled together in **fig 9.2.** we were able to establish the set of graphs shown in **figs 15.6 to fig 15.10**

Perhaps the immediate fact indicated by these figures is the amount by which the velocity is raised when the barrel length is increased. Although we were only able to extend our .22 barrels, the same situation would obviously have existed had we been able to do the same with the other calibres. The muzzle energy also benefits from a heavy projectile, in other words the efficiency of the system increases with a heavier pellet, also the muzzle energy increases as the calibre is enlarged even though the weight of the pellet remains about the same in each case.

From our previous description of the projector it is obvious that the figures from which the above graphs were drawn are based on ideal conditions; that is there were no corners or breech constrictions in the way of the airflow. A more conventional rifle design would probably not yield the same efficiency.

0.177, 20" Long Barrel

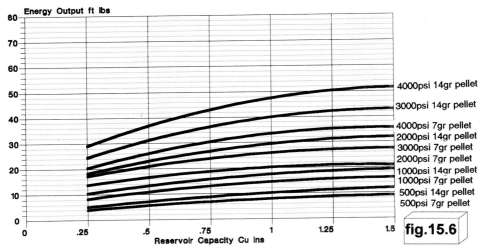

fig.15.6

0.22, 20" Long Barrel

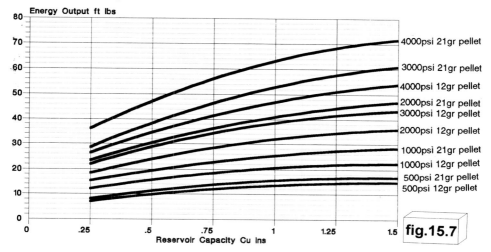

fig.15.7

0.22, 38" Long Barrel

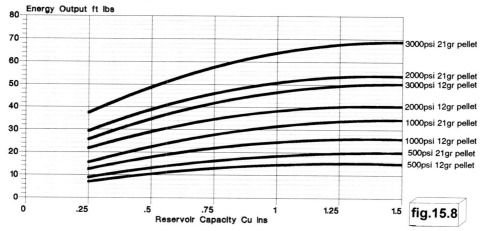

fig.15.8

The Air Gun from Trigger to Target

0.22, 50" Long Barrel

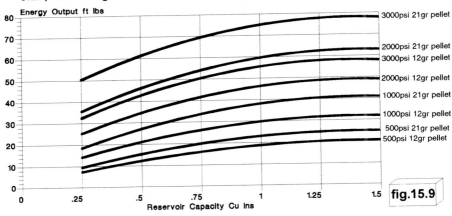

fig.15.9

0.25, 20" Long Barrel

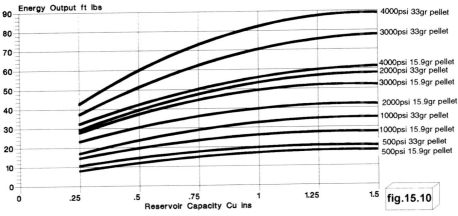

fig.15.10

Chapter 16
RELEASE VALVES AND REGULATORS

The control of the release of the air from the reservoir into the barrel behind the pellet is one of the most difficult design areas of a pneumatic. Ideally the amount of air released at each shot should be capable of driving each pellet at exactly the same velocity whatever the pressure remaining in the reservoir.

Over the years several systems have been developed which aim to accomplish this ideal. They may be divided into two separate groups, the first being the "total loss" or "dump" system, the second the "knock-open" system. In the first scheme all the air that has been pumped into the reservoir is released when the gun is fired, while in the second only a small amount of the stored air is released at each shot. Air cartridges, single stroke pneumatics and certain pump-ups fall into the first group while pre-charged pneumatics and a few pump-ups are in the second.

Pump-up pneumatics which dump their whole charge at each shot can offer remarkably consistent shot to shot velocity, just as long as the number of pump strokes remains constant for each charging, the same remarks apply to air cartridges when they are individually charged by hand.

Most sporting rifles operate on the pre-charged principle and are designed with knock-open valves to release only a small amount of their stored air at each shot, thus offering a large number of shots from each charge. The knock-open system relies upon a hammer in the form of a spring loaded plunger to tap the release valve open for a very short time at each shot. This allows a blast of compressed air to pass through the valve and into the barrel every time the gun is cocked and fired. However, unless the valve and its surrounding chamber is cleverly designed the velocity will vary widely as the air in the reservoir becomes exhausted.

The early airguns and aircanes were built around a fairly sophisticated lock system which forced the valve to open a set distance at every shot. The gun was cocked with a key, or by pulling back a hammer similar to the cock which held the flint in a flint lock. This compressed a leaf spring which when released operated a lever system to force the valve open. The mechanism was expensive to make, requiring hours of machining and hand work before it operated properly, it is not used in any gun today. However, the old system did offer a certain amount of automatic regulation because as the air pressure in the reservoir fell it did not close the valve so rapidly allowing more air into the barrel.

Paul Giffard took out a patent in 1891 for a gas operated rifle. Although his gun was powered by carbon dioxide he still had the problem of releasing a small amount at each shot. Rather than build an expensive lock system like his predecessors, Giffard used a spring loaded hammer to knock the valve open just enough to release the required amount of gas. He even took it a stage further by fitting a control stud which limited the distance by which the hammer struck the valve open; he could therefore adjust the power of his shots very easily. But it must be realised that in employing CO_2 as a propellant Giffard had an advantage over the use of air because as long as there is liquified gas in the reservoir and the temperature remains uniform, then the pressure also remains constant. Had he used air, the pressure would have fallen slightly after each shot.

Variations on the Giffard system are now used in most pre-charged air rifles today. The hammer slides inside the body tube behind the valve, it has a spring at its back which is compressed as the gun is cocked. When the trigger is pulled the hammer flies forward to knock the valve open, it is then immediately closed by a spring and also by the air pressure within the reservoir. This cycle may be repeated over and over again until the air in the reservoir is exhausted.

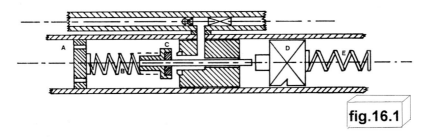

fig.16.1

In the diagram (**fig 16.1**) the reservoir **A** is charged to high pressure through a non return inlet valve, usually placed at the other end of the reservoir. The exhaust valve **C** is held firmly closed by spring **B** and also by the pressure within the reservoir. When the gun is to be fired the hammer **D** is pulled back, compressing spring **E**. Upon release by the trigger, the hammer flies forward and knocks the valve momentarily off its seating allowing a blast of air past the valve and up through the port to drive the pellet along the barrel.

In most designs the hammer is cocked as the bolt is pulled back to load the pellet, a small peg engages with the hammer as the bolt handle is raised, as the bolt is withdrawn the hammer is pulled back with it into the cocked position. This convenient layout also makes the rifle very safe because as long as the bolt is open the pellet cannot be discharged. If the trigger is inadvertently released with the bolt open, the hammer will have to carry the bolt forward with it and in so doing will lose so much of its energy that it will not be able to open the valve fully. Air that manages to pass the valve will be vented harmlessly at the back of the pellet and out through the breech.

In this illustration of a somewhat simplistic system, the rifle would have a very non linear characteristic, in other words the shots would not be of equal velocity. In all probability, if the reservoir is filled to 3,000 PSI, the first shots will slowly increase in velocity until a peak is reached, after which the velocity will steadily fall away as the reservoir is emptied.

Individual manufacturers have modified this system so as to achieve better regulation of the velocity. By altering the basic design of the valve and its housing, also by adjusting the weight of the hammer and the power of its driving spring, many shots of near equal velocity may be obtained. **Fig 16.2** shows how the velocity is likely to rise until the optimum reservoir pressure is reached for the particular rifle, after that the velocity falls slightly as each shot is fired. The successful design and shape of the valve and its housing are subject to the laws of very fast moving air. In most instances however, they are the result of experience, together with inspired trial and error.

Clearly the valve layout shown in **fig 16.1** could be altered to operate as a dumping system, though normally the dump system is only employed in single stroke or pump-up pneumatics. Normally a gun designed to dump its charge at each shot, has a drastically reduced reservoir capacity otherwise the volume of high pressure air available is too great to be used efficiently. Very often this is a fault with pneumatic pistols, especially the pump-up design, the large volume of air cannot be used efficiently within the short length barrel and the excess air discharges with much noise after the pellet has left the muzzle. The characteristics of the hammer and spring must also be different in a dump system because they must be capable of fully opening the valve and holding it open to allow all the stored air to escape at each shot.

The success of any pneumatic largely depends on the choice of the material used for the face of the exhaust valve. It must be soft enough to allow it to bed firmly onto its seating, that is the seating must be able to indent itself into the face material when the valve is closed and under pressure. Equally it must not be too soft, in which case the seating will indent too deeply into the face and will not part easily or quickly from its seating when the hammer knocks it open. Experience has shown that when the working pressure of the gun is high a hard valve material is preferable, whereas in those instances where the pressure is low, a softer face offers a more dependable seal. Over the years we have found that PTFE is an exceptionally suitable material throughout a wide range of pressures, it accepts a satisfactory sealing indent from the seating, while at the same time has the great advantage of being able to absorb small particles of grit without leaking.

Regulated Shots

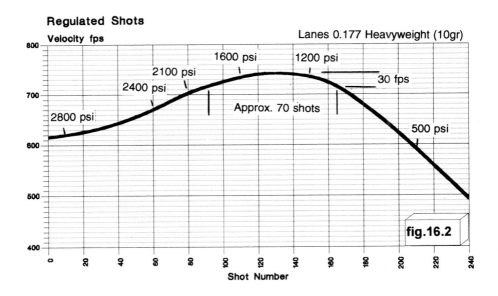

fig.16.2

The valve face material itself must be held firmly on its mounting stem otherwise the high pressure within the reservoir may cause the material to remain firmly pressed against the exhaust port while the spindle on which it is mounted travels on without it. In our diagrammatic rifle shown in **fig 16.1** the exhaust valve **C** is shown as a metal cup holding the face material within it, though in some designs the valve's head is machined in one piece from the chosen material. In this instance the edges of the cup would also be rolled inwards to grip the face material which might also be threaded and bonded onto the spindle together with the cup itself, this firm airtight joint is necessary because the pressure on it is considerable. If any air gets into the joint the facing material will certainly be dragged from its cup when the gun is fired. For instance, suppose the maximum diameter of the sealing face around the port is $^3/_8$" and the reservoir pressure is 3,000 PSI, then the pressure holding the valve onto its seating would be about 600 Lbs. This is the pressure the hammer must overcome to open the valve and is certainly high enough to destroy a fragile valve.

The hammer, its stroke and the power of its spring are three further crucial factors influencing the success of the knock-open system. If they are not chosen correctly the hammer will not open the valve sufficiently to allow the required volume of air to escape. This implies that the momentum of the hammer must be correct if the system is to work correctly. Momentum, as we already know is the product of mass and velocity. But that, in this instance, is not altogether the full story. If the spring is too powerful and the hammer therefore light, the thrust of the spring will probably be great enough to overcome the thrust of the valve closing spring **B** when the reservoir is empty. This means that the exhaust valve must always be closed by cocking the hammer before charging the reservoir. Also, it is probable that when the gun is fired the exhaust valve **C** will be capable of driving the hammer back against its spring as it closes, allowing it to return again fast enough to discharge a second shot. This sequence may repeat itself over again until the air charge has nearly exhausted itself.

If, on the other hand, a heavy hammer and a weak spring are employed, the stroke of the hammer may have to be extended to allow it to achieve the necessary momentum to open the valve. This is because if the mass of the hammer is doubled while the power of the spring remains the same then the momentum of the system will be increased by only fifty percent. This may also result in the blow of the hammer being felt throughout the rifle. However, in practice the compromise between hammer mass and spring strength is not difficult to establish, we have set out the pitfalls if either are very badly chosen.

During a study we carried out some years ago we realised that the easiest way in which the power of a simple pneumatic could be altered is by adjusting the amount by which the hammer opens the valve. We arranged a stop screw inside the hammer so that only the end of the screw made contact with the valve spindle; the power could be altered depending on the position of the screw relative to the front of the hammer. A rubber buffer placed around the valve spindle acted on the rim of the hammer as a stop to absorb the excess energy in the hammer once it had opened the valve. This system offers a simple method of varying the power of a pneumatic without radical alteration to the mechanism every time adjustments are required.

Where the rifle or pistol is designed on the dump system for competition shooting, the air is normally released by a more sophisticated valve system than a knock open valve. When the trigger is pulled the valve is opened by a separate spring loaded lever system and must be manually closed again before the gun is re-cocked. The energy expended in opening the valve by this system is not so great as in the simpler knock-open system, therefore the whole gun is subject to less disturbance when it is fired and the trigger pull is very light. Of course this system may only be applied to guns designed to dump their full charge at each shot.

The difficulties of producing constant velocities from a recharged rifle led Mr. John Ford of Sportsmatch to ask us if we could develop a rifle which would overcome this problem and therefore make the rifle consistent enough for Field Target competitions. We tackled the problem by developing a mechanism which might be called an *"refilling, dump"* system. The charge from a secondary reservoir is fully discharged at each shot, but that air is replaced from a main reservoir every time the gun is re-cocked.

In the diagram (**fig 16.3**) the rifle, named **GC2**, is shown ready to fire, there is a pellet in the breech and the bolt is closed. Chamber **A** is full of air at about 3,000 PSI, while chamber **C** is at a pressure of about 1,500 PSI. This air cannot escape because it is trapped between valve **B** and the special seal **D** around the valve spindle **E**. The pressure is forcing **E** to move backwards, but it is held by its end piece **G** and the thimble shaped cup **F** which are separated by the control spring. **F** cannot move backwards because it is held by the sear **H**.

When the trigger is released sear **H** is forced down by the air pressure thrusting **E** backwards taking **F** and **G** with it, this allows the front face of the valve spindle **E** to uncover the end of the transfer port allowing the charge of air to pass through it and into the barrel.

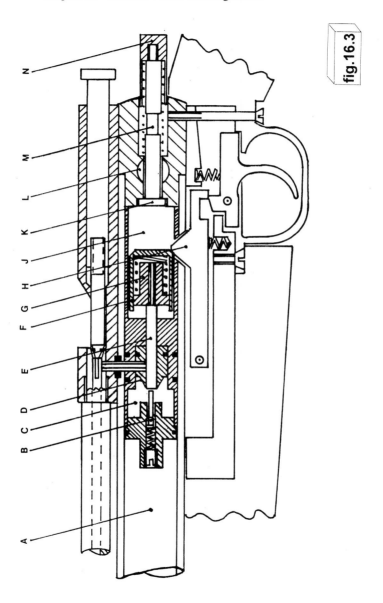

fig.16.3

Before the rifle can be fired again chamber **C** must be refilled from the main reservoir **A** by pressing the charging button **N** inwards until the spring loaded cross bolt **L**, or safety catch, engages with the groove **M** cut into the recharging pin **K**. This locks pin **K** in its forward position where it will reposition the thimble **F** forward, and well beyond the sear **H**. At the same time the valve spindle **E** and its end piece **G** will be moved forward under the influence of the spring. At this point the end of the valve spindle will make contact with the end of the control valve **B** and force it off its seating. Air will now pass slowly through the control valve to fill chamber **C**. As soon as the pressure in **C** reaches a predetermined point the spindle **E** will be forced backwards compressing the spring located inside the thimble **F**, in so doing the control valve **B** will close and the pressure inside chamber **C** will remain constant. The valve assembly **E** and **G** is now held in a balanced condition between the air pressure in **C** and the thrust of the control spring which is trapped between **G** and **F**. The thimble **F** is at this stage still supported by the pin **K** which is held in position by the cross bolt **L**.

The rifle is now charged and ready to fire once the pellet is positioned in the breech and the bolt closed on it. Pressure on the end of **L** releases **K** and **N** which are returned outwards by the light spring inside **N**. At the same time parts **E**, **G**, **H** and the control spring all move backwards until **F** comes up against the sear **H**. This movement causes a gap to form between the end of the valve spindle **E** and the charging valve **B** ensuring that no more air can possibly enter **C**. All the components are now back in their original positions ready for the next shot.

Since air has been drawn from the main reservoir the pressure within it must have fallen slightly, but this will make no difference to the power available for the next shot just so long as the pressure remaining in the reservoir is greater than that required by the secondary chamber **C** to position the valve spindle correctly. Summing up, the system works by having four distinct positions of the valve spindle **E**. Charging, charged, awaiting discharge and discharged.

The success of *GC2* led other manufacturers to design rifles having similar characteristics but without the sophistication of *GC2*. They looked at the possibility of using a knock open valve system but incorporating a pressure regulator so that each shot would be of the same velocity.

Fig 16.4 shows a regulator in diagrammatic form. Referring to **fig 16.1**. It would be placed in the reservoir directly in front of the exhaust valve **C** with its base plug **L** in the proximity of the end of valve spring **A**. The 'O' ring **D** provides the seal whereby air cannot pass along between the regulator's body and the inside of the rifle's reservoir tube.

The purpose of the regulator is to ensure that the pressure of the air at the exhaust valve is always constant irrespective of the pressure within the main reservoir, provided of course that the main pressure is greater than that to which the regulator is set. It works in the following manner:. High pressure air enters past the valve **B** and flows out through port **F** to fill the space in the gun's secondary reservoir in front of the closed exhaust valve. As the pressure increases the piston **G** inside the regulator's body moves backwards compressing the spring **J**. Valve **B** is attached by a screw thread and sealing 'O' ring to the piston **G**. The piston's rearward movement closes the valve **B** against the sealing ring **C**. The piston **G** moves freely backwards because there is a small volume of uncompressed air trapped inside it, sealed in by the metal bellows **K**.

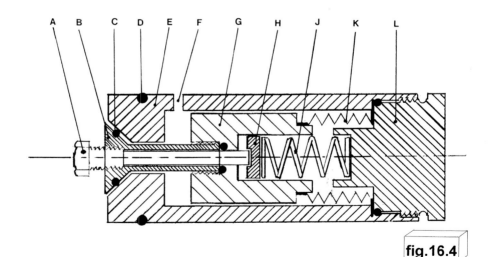

fig.16.4

Once valve **B** has closed no more air can enter the secondary reservoir through the regulator and that trapped within it will be at a preset pressure. The preset output pressure of the regulator is controlled by the balance of the air pressure within it acting against the piston and spring **J**, this balance may be varied by adjusting the pressure on the spring. Adjusting screw **A** is provided for just this purpose, screwing it inwards increases the thrust of the spring and therefore the pressure delivered by the regulator. It is important to notice that the 'O' ring around the stem of the adjusting screw must seal this joint perfectly otherwise the air pressure inside the bellows and behind the piston will rise and alter the regulation.

A metal bellows **K** has been chosen for internal sealing rather than an O ring which might have been placed in a groove around the piston's body to seal against its cylinder. The choice of bellows as a seal has been made because it is imperative that the piston is able to move very freely in response to small pressure differences. An 'O' ring in the same situation would tend to become wedged by the pressure between the two moving surfaces restricting the free movement of the piston, resulting in poor regulating characteristics.

We have shown an 'O' ring as the sealing medium at the critical point C. In all probability this ring would exhibit the same problems that we have just mentioned, a more sophisticated valve and seating would be required here rather than the one shown in our over simplified diagram.

It has been our experience that regulators give the most accurate performance if the air is allowed to pass slowly through them, it is for this reason that in **fig 16.3**, the diagram of *GC2*, it will be noticed that the air must pass around the threads of the screw which holds the control valve **B** closed. This restriction ensures that the secondary reservoir is charged very slowly and accurately. The same arguments would apply to the regulator we have shown in **fig 16.4**., clearly a restricting device fitted in front of it would improve its accuracy.

Needless to say a regulator increases the cost of the rifle, they are therefore normally fitted only to expensive rifles designed for competition shooting. It must be pointed out however, that non regulated rifles with carefully designed and constructed exhaust valves are often capable of producing an adequate number of close velocity shots for most shooting requirements.

In a rifle fitted with a regulator, the exhaust valve, its closing spring also the hammer and its spring, must all work correctly relative to each other. They must operate so that on firing, most of the air is released, but since the regulator will immediately start refilling the empty secondary reservoir once the shot has been fired, the exhaust valve must return to its closed position very fast so that the fresh supply of incoming air will not escape through it. This design could well be called an "automatically refilling dump" system, if such a name were necessary.

Chapter 16 - Release Valves and Regulators

Chapter 17
CARBON DIOXIDE

Before diving became such a popular sport the only reasonable way of operating rifles and pistols from a portable source of compressed power was by the use of carbon dioxide. At the end of the last century Paul Giffard patented his beautifully made guns which operated on interchangeable gas cylinders; later many other gun makers especially those in America adopted the same system, probably Crosman being the best known. It is still a popular propellent system in America, but seldom used in this country.

The main reason why carbon dioxide is not popular in the UK is that its employment makes the gun subject to Fire Arms Certification, in other words it is classed as a rimfire or centrefire arm and therefore its use is restricted. In the States the gas is cheaper and more readily available than it is here. At the same time cold weather reduces the velocity of the shot, often to an unacceptable value.

We have experimented with guns operated by carbon dioxide, or more often known by its chemical formula CO_2, normally purchasing it in the steel bulbs sold for making soda-water. We have always found it to be very unsatisfactory as a propellent and because of its low pressure it does not produce better velocities than those attainable with compressed air. It is also heavier than air, and having a higher viscosity makes a "sticky" gas which does not flow as freely as air.

Carbon dioxide has very different properties than air. **Fig.17.1** is a graph which indicates its chief characteristic. At any point below the line the gas is a liquid, while at any point above it, it is a vapour. This means that a cylinder of the gas at a temperature of say, 20° Centigrade will be at a pressure of 812 PSI. If the temperature of the cylinder is raised then part of the liquid gas will boil off to increase the pressure within the cylinder to suit the new temperature.

If some of the vapour is allowed out of the cylinder, perhaps to fire a pellet then obviously the pressure inside the cylinder will fall and liquid will then boil off to replace the pressure but in so doing it will need heat. This heat will be obtained from the remainder of the liquid and its container, in so doing it will reduce its temperature; the reduction in temperature will cause the pressure in the cylinder to fall for a short time until the temperature has been restored by gathering heat from the atmosphere.

The Air Gun from Trigger to Target

Carbon Dioxide

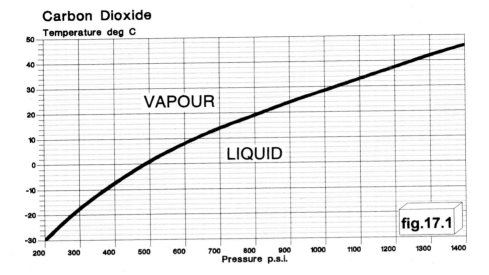

fig.17.1

Airgunners want the maximum pressure at all times, so having to wait until the cylinder has warmed up again in the sunshine is a somewhat frustrating delay. The suggested figure of 20° Centigrade (68° F), the sort of temperature we should expect on a hot Summer's day in this country but as we have already seen the gas at this temperature will be at a pressure of only 812 PSI, a pressure which is not very high when compared to that obtainable from a diver's cylinder.

Carbon dioxide is not an easy gas to seal into its containers, many of the materials with which we are familiar for sealing air are not suitable for the gas. For instance 'O' rings which are made for air will absorb CO_2 and expand until they look like caterpillars, polyurethane is the most suitable material for these rings.

Many users of pneumatic rifles are familiar with the simple technique of filling them from an air cylinder, or even refilling a small cylinder from a larger one. It is a straight forward operation, connect the two together and open the valves while keeping an eye on the gauge to check the pressure build up. But it is not so simple with CO_2. To ensure the empty cylinder, or gun, receives its maximum quantity of the gas its temperature must first be reduced by cooling it in the deep freeze or refrigerator. If the gun is not cool the incoming gas, in its liquid form, will immediately turn to vapour on entering the relatively hot gun. The vapour will then fill the reservoir and pressurise it to the point where no further liquid is allowed to enter it. As long as the reservoir is cool the liquid will enter it without difficulty; of course this means that the charging cylinder of CO_2 is placed above the reservoir, preferably in the upside down position so that the outlet valve is covered with liquid.

Guns using CO_2 always employ a knock open valve to release the gas into the barrel, Paul Giffard probably being the first gunmaker to use this device. However there is a difficulty, especially if the gun is fired pointing upwards, the valve will allow liquid into the barrel where it will immediately try to change to vapour as its pressure falls. Inevitably it will not be able to gain heat fast enough to complete its transformation and part of the liquid will be cooled even further to form a solid, resulting in a further reduction in velocity. This solid will be ejected in the form of CO_2 snow after the pellet has left the muzzle.

Some modern pistol designs can use CO_2 to its best advantage because the throw away gas cylinder is concealed in the butt, well below the valve, from which point it can offer a plentiful supply of vapour. CO_2 has also been tried with doubtful success as a propellant in rifles designed for high accuracy match shooting, but here again its drawbacks seem to have overcome its advantages and its popularity has declined.

Having spent so much of this chapter discussing the negative side of carbon dioxide it is time to redress the balance by pointing out situations where it has advantages. The individualist gun maker John Bowkett has in recent years made some very successful and unique arms using the gas. His designs ensure that no liquid reaches the valve, reducing the detrimental cooling effects, he also employs larger than standard calibres which offer greater efficiency from the CO_2.

Probably the greatest advantage of CO_2 is the number of shots that can be obtained from a relatively small volume of liquid. A large volume of vapour is formed from a remarkably small quantity of liquid, so provided the temperature of the system remains constant the pressure too remains constant, offering a high consistency in the gun's velocity, provided of course that the shots are not fired rapidly enough to reduce the temperature.

Chapter 17 - Carbon Dioxide

The large volume of gas available from a charge of liquid CO_2 offers enough energy to power semi automatic rifles and pistols, probably the best example of these was the Crosman 600 pistol. Here the gas not only propelled the pellet but also operated the pellet feed mechanism that faultlessly collected a pellet from the inline magazine and positioned it in the breech ready for the next shot. The magazine held about ten pellets which could be fired one after another as fast as the trigger could be pulled.

Taking an overall view of the role of carbon dioxide in airgunning, we feel it is reasonable to say that it has many advantages in the field of not-too-serious-shooting, but when high power, high consistency and high accuracy are concerned precharged pneumatics have all the advantages.

Chapter 18
PELLETS AND PELLET TESTING

Early airgun ammunition consisted of darts, ball, or what we now call "Cat Slugs". Just why and how they got that name is not clear, but we hope the obvious reason is not correct. None of these types of missile could possibly reach the standards of accuracy that we expect today, but since the guns were neither powerful, nor in many instances had rifled barrels, early small bore domestic air guns were little more than toys. We use the word domestic to separate them from the large bore, ball or butt reservoir rifles that were as good, and probably more reliable than the flintlocks in general use during the early years of shooting.

The date and maker of the first diabolo shaped pellet seems to be lost in the mists of time, we feel that they were perhaps made by an airgun enthusiast who also played badminton, or baddledore and shuttlecock as it will have been known in those days. He will have noticed that shuttlecocks always flew with their heavy nose forwards, controlled by the lightweight feathered tail, also that they did not deviate from their original flight line except in a wind. If this shape could be reproduced in lead it might fly with greater accuracy in his smooth bore gun than any other pellet available to him at that time.

Most waisted pellets have small ribs running round their skirts and under their heads. In many instances these are put there by the pellet making machine as it rolls the waist into the cup shaped pellet blank after it has been punched from the lead strip. An alternative system by which pellets are made, is to force the lead between dies into which the exact shape of the pellet has been formed. In some instances these pellets too have ribs on their tails, in which case they are very clear and geometrically perfect. Normally though, the pellets manufactured by this process have very smooth surfaces and are exceptionally well finished, the joint line left by the dies being only just discernable, they therefore command a higher price and are usually more consistent and accurate in their performance than the previous type. The ribs themselves make no difference to the accuracy of the ammunition, if it is inaccurate the cause lies elsewhere. It might however be argued that the ribs create an extra air disturbance, absorbing rotational energy as they fly. We have never been able to either prove or disprove this statement. However ill effects would seem unlikely since the air flowing over that part of the pellet will be slightly rarefied due to the head and tail flanges and therefore any effect caused by the ribs will be minimal.

Originally airgun ammunition was made in three calibres: .177", .22" and .25", these were also known as No.1 bore, No.2 bore and No. 3 bore respectively. But for a long period .25 fell from popularity, probably because it was found that the guns and pellets available in that calibre tended to be inaccurate. Also, if the British limit on muzzle energy was to be adhered to, the velocity had to be kept low because of their heavy weight. However in recent years there has been an increase in interest in this calibre because a few rifle manufacturers have decided to build high powered models which although subject to Fire Arm Certification are capable of propelling these heavy pellets at reasonable velocities. There can be no doubt as to the value of a large heavy pellet when it comes to vermin control, the small diameter of the .177 often acts like a hypodermic needle, penetrating the quarry without causing enough damage to stop it; whereas the .25 will stop most pests instantly. The general rule, ".22 for fur and .177 for feather" has often been suggested on the basis that the smaller pellet will penetrate a layer of feathers better than a large one, while .22 usually humanely kills fur covered airgun quarry.

Another calibre which has had a varying degree of success is .20. Followers of this calibre claim that it has all the advantages of both .177 and .22 and few of the disadvantages. But since not many rifles are made to accept it we will say little more about it; mainly because, good or bad, we did not use it in any of our experiments. Steel darts have no place in serious airgunning since their passage through the barrel at high speed can do little for the quality of the rifling; though they still have their place in fairgrounds where they are fired through smooth bored guns or worn out rifles.

Although many attempts have been made to improve on the performance of pellets, there are none available today which are superior in cost, availability and accuracy to challenge the supremacy of the lead diabolo in its many forms. Each year new types of pellet are launched onto the market, but the vast majority of them are only slight variations of the existing waisted form. The established brands of diabolo pellets are produced with a variety of different shaped heads, round, dome, flat, pointed or even hollow. The flat headed variety is preferred by the target marksmen because they punch clean holes in the cards making scoring more precise; also they are usually the most accurate over shorter ranges. Dome headed pellets would seem to be the most popular and are chosen by the majority of users. Nevertheless the manufacturers of each different pellet shape make exaggerated claims as to its excellency, but that is understandable in any industry. The global production of pellets is a very difficult figure to establish accurately, but it certainly runs into many, many millions each year.

Diabolo pellets are remarkably accurate even when they are not spinning, a fact easily demonstrated by firing them at short range through a smooth bore barrel. However, it has one great drawback, its shape generates a large amount of drag as it passes through the air. This resistance means that the pellet has a limited range relative to that which it would enjoy if it were more streamlined and could cut through the air easier. The excessive resistance inevitably increases the flight time which in turn allows the pellet to lose more height during the time it takes to travel between the muzzle and the target; this in turn means that the marksman has to judge the range very accurately and adjust his sights accordingly.

Quite obviously it would be advantageous if an air gunner could test the quality of his pellets before he goes out shooting, especially if there are valuable prizes to be won in a competition. Several systems have been developed by which match pellets are inspected and graded with a view to selecting the best before each meeting in the hope of eliminating "flyers", (those pellets which for no obvious reason take off on a completely random course ruining an otherwise perfect score). The selection of competition grade pellets is normally preceded by washing the whole batch in detergent to remove oil or lead particles before drying them thoroughly in a warm oven. Each pellet is then individually weighed to an accuracy of about one tenth of a grain, those falling outside this very close tolerance being rejected for the competition, but retained for future practice.

Although commercial scales may be bought for weighing pellets, a simple device may be made which can weigh to an accuracy of a quarter of a grain. **Fig 18.1** shows a set of these scales, they are simply a narrow strip of thin metal kinked in the middle and balanced over half a razor blade. The weights are Rexel Bambi staples which weigh exactly a quarter of a grain each.

The next test to carry out is the gauging of the diameter of each pellet by dropping it inside the case of a cheap ball point pen after the ink tube has been removed. The bore of these pens is slightly tapered so each pellet will take up a different position depending on the diameter of its skirt. Two slightly separated marks are made on the outside of the tube and the selected pellets are then expected to position themselves between these two. Although this may seem to be a very simplistic method of measuring pellets it is in fact a very satisfactory one because the use of a normal micrometer tends to distort the soft lead giving undersize readings.

fig.18.1

Since the skirt diameter of any pellet worth its salt will be slightly larger than the head, the pellet should move in a circle when rolled on a smooth surface by gently blowing on it. Obviously the greater the difference between the two diameters the smaller the described circle will be. Assuming that the head diameter is correct for that barrel, pellets which roll in a small circle are likely to be tight in the bore because the tail is large; those which describe a large circle will be less tight. However, it must be remembered that some brands have thicker lead at the tail than others, in which case a smaller tail diameter is acceptable otherwise the lead will be too firm to collapse correctly into the bore. Those pellets which roll in a straight line would be useless except in a low power rifle operating in the *blowpipe* phase.

While the pellet is rolling it is well worth observing whether it rolls smoothly or not, if it moves in a series of jerks it is probably out of balance or the tail flange is distorted. Also the pellet should not appear to wobble as it rolls, especially the flange of the tail; in simple words, it must "look right", the eye being and exceptionally good "inspector". If the tail edge of a pellet lies oblique to the body it will certainly leave the muzzle out of square, with disastrous effects on its accuracy.

Just how valuable these tests really are in increasing the score during the competition is open to argument, it is possible that the main benefit is psychological rather than practical - a good case of "mind over matter". We set out to construct equipment with which we could examine, compare and study the characteristics of various pellets in the hope of determining why some brands, or shapes, are more accurate than others.

Fig 18.2 shows a device by which a pellet can be made to revolve at very high speeds and then dropped onto its head to continue spinning on a sheet of glass, like a top. The pellet is first positioned in the cup at the end of the hollow spindle, then while suction is applied via the mouthpiece to hold the pellet in place, the current is switched on to the small electric motor. The whole unit including the spinning pellet can then be turned over and the pellet blown from the cup to continue spinning on a flat surface. The accuracy with which it spins, especially as it slows down, is an indicator of the quality of the pellet's balance. Short pellets with heavy tails, that is pellets in which the centre of gravity is fairly far back from the nose, tend to turn over and spin on their sides, but most pellets spin perfectly on their noses, those that are not in balance wobble wildly as they come to a stop. Of course the performance of flat or hollow headed pellets can not be examined by this system.

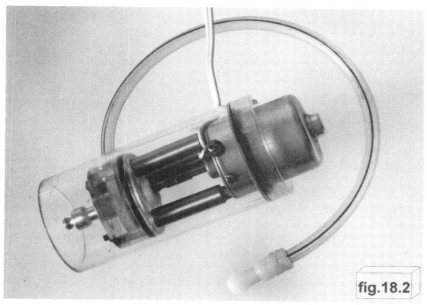

fig.18.2

The Air Gun from Trigger to Target

To establish the position of the centre of gravity of pellets we encased them in resin then faced off each side in a lathe until we were left with a wafer of resin in which a cross section of the centre of the pellet was left visible, **fig 18.3**. We then placed the wafer in the photographic enlarger and printed an oversize image onto thick paper. After cutting round the silhouette we hung it, in turn, on each of two pin holes made at points around its edge, **fig 18.4**. As it hung freely from each point a pencil mark was made on the lower edge at a point indicated by a cotton plumb line hanging from the same supporting pin. This gave us two lines across the silhouette. The centre of gravity is at the point where the two lines cross. In most instances the centre of gravity lies at a point between a third and a half of the pellet's length back from its nose.

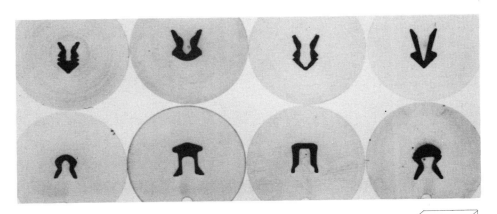

fig.18.3

Very often the value of any test can be increased by purposely exaggerating the error for which we are testing, even checking the effect of damage caused to pellets through carrying them in a tin is worth investigating because it is often not as bad as claimed. In the instance of the spinning pellet, lead may be cut away from one side of the inside; this treatment emphasises the effect of any out of balance error. In other tests, pieces of the pellet can be cut away from the side of the nose or tail to investigate the characteristics of misshaped pellets. We have always been surprised by the large amount of damage that must be done to a pellet before its accuracy is seriously impaired.

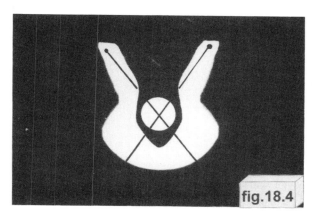

fig.18.4

Wind Tunnel

In describing these various specially made pieces of equipment we are very aware of a saying we often use, *"It is one thing to make a violin, it is quite another to learn to play it"*. By this we mean that the operation of any test apparatus needs patience and careful observation before any benefits will be gained from it.

As part of our investigation into the characteristics of the different pellet shapes we built a small wind tunnel, this is shown in **fig 18.5**. At the base is a vacuum cleaner power unit which draws air down through the long $1^1/_4$" bore tube; the air first flows over the pellet which is mounted on a balance so that its resistance to the passage of the air may be measured.

The balance itself is shown in detail in **fig 18.6**, it will be seen that part of it is inside the tube while the majority is outside. In practice the instrument is placed in the tube without any pellets on it, the air is then drawn down over it while weights are placed on the pan so as to counterbalance the effect of the air drag over the instrument's arms. Two pellets are then placed on the vertical spikes, the one outside the tube counterbalancing the other on the inside. Further weights must then be placed on the pan to counterbalance the increased drag caused by the airflow over the pellet in the tube. It is of course the sum of these new weights which determines the air drag over the pellet.

The Air Gun from Trigger to Target

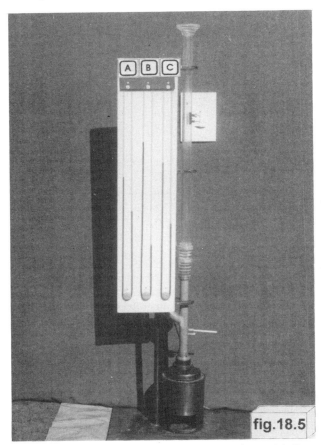

fig.18.5

Further down the tube is a specially shaped constriction called a "venturi" which is coupled to the U tubes mounted on the board, this causes the coloured water in the tubes to take up positions corresponding to the speed of the airflow through the tube and therefore over the pellet.

The 'U' tubes **A**, **B** & **C** are coupled to the tube at various points. **A** registers the pressure between the pellet and the venturi. **B** shows the pressure across the venturi, the left hand leg of the U tube being connected to the constriction of the venturi. **C** indicates the pressure between the power unit and the venturi. Just above the power unit a thermometer may be seen, this measures the temperature of the air travelling through the system.

The figures taken from the difference in the heights of the liquid in each of the tubes forms the basis for calculating the airspeed over the pellet; values for the temperature of the air, also its humidity and the barometric pressure all have to be taken into account before a final velocity figure can be established. The exact procedure for these calculations may be found in the British Standard 1042 (Measurement of Airflow).

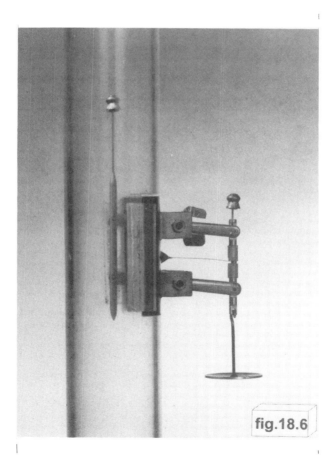

fig.18.6

The maximum velocity attainable in this wind tunnel is about 130 FPS, which is low when compared with a more realistic pellet velocity of about 700 FPS, also it must be remembered that if the velocity of the pellet is doubled the resistance or drag goes up four times. However, calculations show that a blower of at least ten horsepower capacity would be required if the higher velocity were to be realised; such a machine would be far too large for us to contemplate. Nevertheless very interesting and useful comparative figures were obtained from this device in spite of its low velocity.

A selection of pellets is shown in **fig 18.7**, this is a representative collection of shapes together with one or two experimental rounds individually made to study the drag of alternative forms. Examination of the drag figures, which are quoted in grains at a velocity of 133 FPS, show that a model with a long tail such as pellet **S**, as expected, produces far less drag than the normal diabolo pellet which finishes with a sharp edged skirt.

| Pellet. | Drag (grains) | |
	.22	.177
A	16.0	---
B	---	10.0
C	13.5	---
D	13.5	8.0
E	18.0	11.0
F	16.5	10.0
G	19.0	11.0
H	---	9.0
J	---	9.5
K	13.5	8.0
L	---	8.5
M	---	9.5
N	---	10.0
O	11.5	---
P	16.5	10.0
Q	10.5	---
R	12.0	---
S	9.0	---
T	11.0	---

Chapter 18 - Pellets and Pellet Testing

At a later date various .25 pellets were tested in the wind tunnel and found to produce drag figures between 25 and 30 grains, depending on their design. The main intention of examining these larger calibre rounds was not only to establish their own drag, but also to use them as guinea pigs in a study of alternative shapes. We altered their basic form by filling in the waist, or by building up their nose or tail with Plasticine. However at the modest air speed attainable in this tunnel the drag differences were virtually undetectable.

Shooting experience with experimental pellets machined with streamlined tails showed us that inspite of having reduced air resistance they were not accurate. Clearly another case in airgunning where a compromise must be struck.

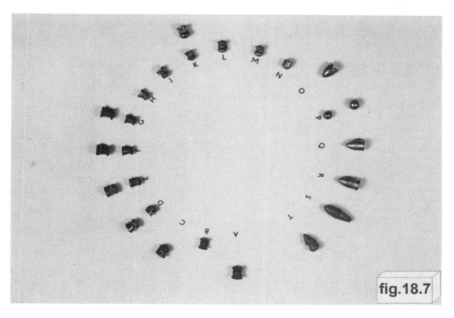

fig.18.7

We then constructed another type of wind tunnel, shown diagrammatically in **fig 18.8**. This again is built around a vacuum cleaner power unit, but in this instance the air is blown up through the vertical tapered tube. A pellet dropped into the tube will take up its own natural position riding on the rising air current. The velocity of the air can be adjusted by altering the speed of the motor so that the pellet settles at a point as high in the tube as possible without undue bouncing or wobble.

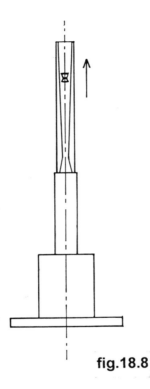

fig.18.8

The production of the tapered tube caused us plenty of headaches not only in its construction, but also in its dimensions. The final model was moulded using transparent resin; it is about twelve inches long, the bore tapering from a quarter of an inch up to five eighths at its greatest diameter. The outside diameter of the tube is about one and a quarter inches.

Experiments with this tube soon showed that pellets with flat faces, a small waist near the head, and sharp edges at their tails, were the most stable whilst flying in the tube. All these factors had produced noticeably high drag when flown in the previous tunnel. Other more streamlined pellets would bob up and down, turn sideways or even fly upside down. Certainly if the centre of air resistance is in front of the centre of gravity the pellet will tumble in the tube and is useless as a projectile unless it is spun by the rifling in the barrel. Looking again at a shuttlecock, it is plain that the centre of air resistance is well back amongst the tail feathers while the centre of gravity is forward towards the head, hence it is happy to fly nose forward in a stable manner without the benefit of gyroscopic stabilisation imparted by spin.

At the same time experiments can be carried out on existing pellets by adding parts made from Plasticine or other moulding material, not forgetting that the slight extra weight of the additional parts will influence the pellet's position in the tube. Alternatively totally new shapes may be machined and flight tested in the tube.

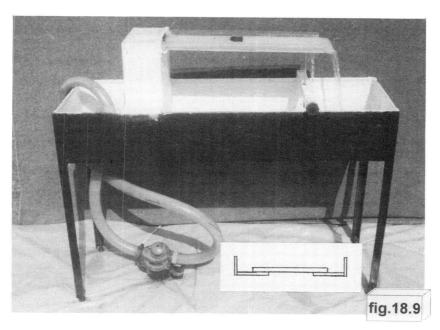

fig.18.9

Water - Table

The contradictory characteristics indicated by the previous two experiments led us to fabricate a water table in the hope of being able to better understand the airflow over pellets. **Fig 18.9** shows the final machine; the circulating pump is on the floor, it takes water from the bottom of the tank and lifts it to the higher tank from where it flows in a steady stream down the smooth flat Perspex table, covering the surface to an equal depth as it goes. A small scale cross section of the table itself is shown let into the main picture, this shows the gutters either side of the of the plane over which the water flows. The gutters prevent confusing random waves from forming and being reflected back from the upright walls. The output from the pump is variable, as also is the tilt of the table; by adjusting these two, both the speed and depth of the water running over the table may be altered to give a clearly visible pattern of waves in the water similar to that which would be generated by a pellet in air.

Water being far denser than air allows the behaviour of bodies moving through air to be studied at lower and more manageable velocities. The waves generated by a pellet as it flies can be examined as the water flow is accelerated from normal subsonic velocities right through the sound barrier and into the supersonic region. This wide range of velocities can be mimicked by simply increasing the tilt of the table and at the same time raising the flow from the pump to compensate for the extra speed of the water down the table.

Water flowing over a pellet at a subsonic velocity is shown in **fig 18.10**, the majority of the disturbance is ahead of the pellet caused by the large wave which travels along with it causing a disturbance in the surrounding water generating more waves which fan out to the sides of the pellet. However the formation of all waves requires energy and this must come from the pellet itself, the loss is called "forebody drag".

The speed of the water has been increased in **fig 18.11** and is now flowing over the pellet at a simulated supersonic velocity. The compression waves at the front of the pellet have moved closer and bunched up together to form a shock wave, while the angle they form at the tail has closed up too. At Mach 1, the local speed of sound, the angle formed by the waves is 90 degrees, but this then closes up further as the velocity increases.

We wanted to amplify the conditions at subsonic velocities so as to make the effect of the wave clearer; we multiplied all the pellet's dimensions by five then cut a model out of thick plastic.(**fig 18.12**). A small quantity of aluminium powder in the water confirms the zone of compressed air being forced along by the pellet as it flies. This zone is made clearly visible because the powder drops out of suspension as the water stops in front of the pellet, the powder then forms an arc around the nose. Similarly in flight, as the pellet's velocity increases the zone moves nearer the nose until eventually at the speed of sound it turns into a shock wave.

Air robs a pellet of its kinetic energy all the time it is in flight. We have already looked in detail at forbody drag, which it must be admitted is of less importance while the projectile is travelling at subsonic velocities. At the sort of velocities encountered in airguns the drag and disturbance at the tail of the pellet or "base-drag" is of greater significance. Base-drag is generated because air cannot get into the back of the flying pellet fast enough to fill the space left by the advancing tail, the pellet is in effect being sucked backwards as it flies.

If a dinner plate is held at an angle under a running tap it will be found that the water can be persuaded to flow along its underside without difficulty. The water appears to be flowing upside down, clinging to the plate as it goes. Air clings to a moving pellet in just the same manner and in so doing it resists the pellet's forward travel by what is known as "skin friction". A pellet does in fact drag a thin layer of air along with it as it flies, this layer also drags another layer of slightly slower moving air along with it too, which drags a slower layer etc. But it all adds up to a reduction in velocity as air is pulled along with the pellet; in all probability skin friction is the greatest of the three power robbers encountered by a diabolo pellet travelling at sub sonic velocities, followed in order by base drag and then forebody drag.

The flow over a pellet is further complicated by the narrowness of the pellet's waist which causes energy consuming turbulence; on one occasion when we were using the water table a tiny particle of dirt became trapped between the head and tail of the pellet and continued to spin like a top, locked firmly in the eddy current.

Destructive Testing

The simplest destructive test, and the one we used when we first investigated pellets, is to fire them against a solid piece of steel set at various distances from the rifle. As long as the steel is set so that the pellet hits it square, the interpretation of the damage to the pellet can reveal a considerable amount of information about the pellet's flight also its striking attitude and energy. Great care is necessary throughout, shooting glasses are mandatory! the interpretation of the fired pellets requires thought and experience. However, there is a wealth of knowledge to be extracted from the technique and the benefits are well worth the time, effort and patience.

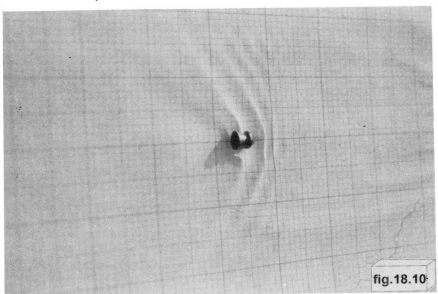

fig.18.10

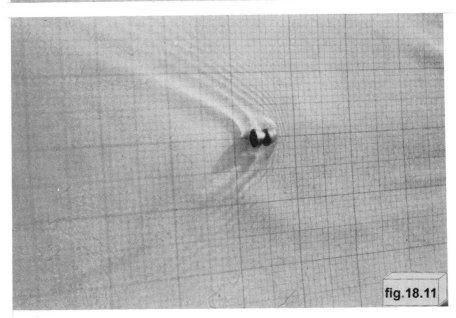

fig.18.11

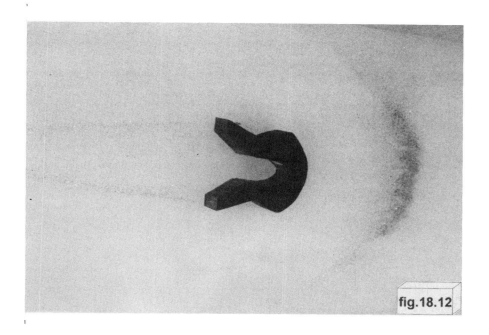

fig.18.12

Pellet Deformation

A very important question which must be asked in airgunning is: "Is the pellet that leaves the muzzle the same as the one that was placed in the breech". The answer is usually, "no", especially at higher velocities. Very often the pellet's tail will have been expanded by the sudden release of high pressure air behind it, altering the pellet's flight characteristics particularly when it is fired at high velocity.

The pellets shown in **fig 18.13** all indicate what is likely to happen to any pellet as it is accelerated along the barrel. Three sample pellets of each type are shown. The first pellet has not been fired, the next on its right was fired through our projector and the one on its right was fired using a spring cylinder on the same projector. The same barrel being used in each instance for both pneumatic and spring propulsion.

Pellet.	Cal.	Weight.	Pneumatic.		Spring.	
			Velocity.	Energy.	Velocity.	Energy.
A	.25	18.8	760	24.0	736	22.6
B	.25	27.5	675	27.8	478	13.9
C	.25	17.6	779	23.7	660	17.0
D	.22	16.5	901	29.7	620	14.1
E	.22	14.2	970	29.6	860	23.3
F	.22	23.4	1051	57.4	580	17.5
G	.177	8.5	1263	30.1	800	12.1
H	.177	7.6	850	12.2	850	12.2
I	.177	8.2	1023	19.1	930	15.7

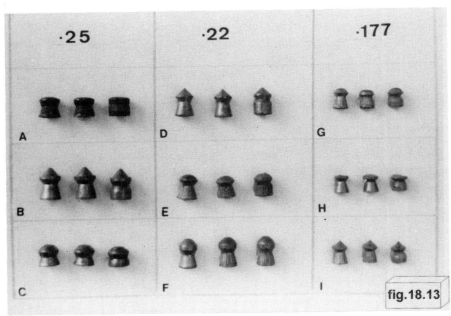

fig.18.13

Study of these pellets and their velocity reveals that no two brands of pellet behave in the same manner. Pellet **A** folded up completely when fired by a spring, yet withstood the pressure when driven by a pneumatic. Pellet **B** showed considerable deformation when fired by a spring, yet a pneumatic caused little expansion even though the velocity was far higher. In general terms a spring gun is more likely to cause damage to a pellet than a pneumatic; though it must be said that air cartridges will often expand pellets' tails too. This appears to be because the pellet is placed immediately in front of the air charge so that it receives the full force of the air when the valve opens.

The amount of the expansion depends on many factors but mainly on the hardness of the lead, also the rate at which the pellet is accelerated. Oscillograms (**fig 18.14**) taken at the same time as the pellets were fired show that they are subjected to an enormous pressure for a very short time in a spring gun operating in the *combustion* phase. Alternatively the pressure behind a pellet in the breech of a pneumatic (**fig 18.15**) is much lower, but the fact that the blast lasts for a considerably longer time accounts for the fact that the pellet is accelerated to a far higher velocity.

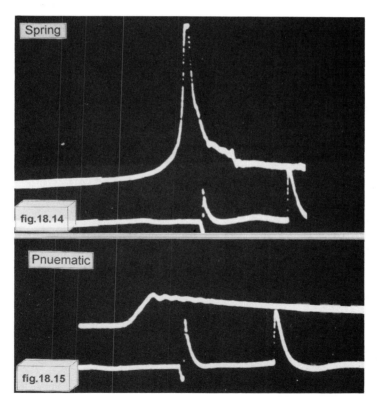

The Air Gun from Trigger to Target

We obviously needed to know how much effect the damage caused by compression would have on the accuracy and flight characteristics of a deformed pellet. We deliberately expanded a number of different brands of pellet by subjecting them to oil at high pressure in a piece of barrel. The resulting pellets would not fly correctly in the wind tunnel of **fig 18.8**, they also showed a reduced drag when tested in the other tunnel of **fig 18.5**. Inevitably the quality of their accuracy was also depleted considerably.

Clearly the pellets shown in **fig.18.13**. had to be stopped gently so as not to increase or alter the deformation caused by firing them. The problem of stopping pellets in mid flight without further damage may be solved in two alternative ways depending on the number to be stopped. If a long study is envisaged requiring many pellets to be examined, we found that table desert jelly is a very satisfactory substance. It should be prepared in the normal manner, but in this instance the quantity of the jelly should be doubled or perhaps trebled relative to the amount of water. The mixture should then be poured into a clear plastic lemonade bottle so that it is three quarters full before allowing it to set while the bottle is lying on its side. Once set, the bottle should be cut away to leave an oblong lump of jelly into which the pellets may be fired. A light coloured jelly, such as lemon, is the best choice because the pellets may be seen clearly and quickly retrieved using thin nosed pliers.

Alternatively, if pellets are only occasionally to be stopped for examination another system, suggested to us by a fellow enthusiast, may be used. A length of three inch diameter plastic drainpipe about two feet long is partially filled with the polyester wadding normally sold for filling cushions. Cotton wool is not as suitable, the fibres are too short and not strong enough to hold the pellets. A pellet fired into the wadding immediately becomes entangled in the long tough fibres and pulls the wad along the tube until it has given up all its energy. Finding the pellet after it has become trapped can be troublesome, especially if it is small, but once the material has been obtained it will last forever. Jelly on the other hand slowly disintegrates and must be discarded after a few days.

Spiralling

It has been suggested that pellets tend to fly in a spiral, like a corkscrew. We never took this idea too seriously because if it is true a pellet can only be accurate at certain points along its trajectory. It was later suggested that the spiral was in fact an illusion, the pellet appearing to spiral as it flew away because the rifle, together with its scope, wobble once the pellet has left the muzzle giving the impression that it is flying away like a corkscrew. However, we put the "spiral phenomena" to the test because if it were really true there would be little future in serious airgunning.

First of all we stretched a strong nylon fishing line from above the muzzle of our projector to a point immediately above the centre of a group of test shots on a target thirty yards away. Using adjustable "gallows" stands we hung four or five sheets of rice paper at equal intervals along the path of the pellet; each sheet having a clear vertical line drawn on it. This vertical line was positioned, using a plumb line, directly under the fishing line. We now had a set of positive reference lines along the pellet's flight path; if a pellet flew in a spiral it would wander either side of these lines as it went. We would not be able to tell whether it moved up or down during its flight, but this did not detract from the test, if the pellet spiralled at all it must do so both vertically and horizontally, describing a corkscrew figure around a central path.

Every one of the shots followed a straight course through the screens making holes on each vertical line. Every shot that is, except one; this one set off in the wrong direction from the start and maintained its error all the way to the target, in other words it was a classic *"flyer".*

On a previous occasion when we carried out a similar experiment over a much longer distance, we came to the same negative conclusion. So it would seem to us that the idea of a "spiralling pellet" is a myth, though it must be said that it is not impossible that a pellet which is very badly out of balance may describe a small spiral about its centre of gravity, but this must remain within the pellet itself. Properly made pellets must fly true, but it is always a pity when a flyer messes up an experiment then disappears never to be found for examination. If a few flyers were caught intact it might be possible to establish exactly what caused them to become "rogues". We could then put a definite answer to the question, "What causes a flyer" ?

We use rice paper when examining pellet flight, it is obtainable from most supermarkets for placing under cakes as they bake. Instead of being fibrous like normal paper its construction is like a thin sheet of dried mashed potato; it is in fact made from potatoes these days and not rice. The potato particles shatter to powder as the pellet passes through leaving a clean hole. The lack of fibre in the sheet means that the pellet will not be deflected from its original course, also this paper offers minimum resistance to the pellet when it strikes, so the velocity is not appreciably reduced as it passes.

We wondered why pellets appear to become less accurate at longer ranges. Various suggestions were made as to why this should be and decided that perhaps one of the reasons might be that they lose rotational energy faster than they lose kinetic energy. In other words they stop spinning before they hit their target; if this is true then it is very likely that they would lose accuracy at the same time.

We proved that they do not stop spinning after a long flight by removing ink from a ball point pen with a straightened out paper clip then smearing some of the sticky ink on one side of the front of a pellet's head. This pellet was then fired at two sheets of ordinary photocopy paper suspended from stands down range, the sheets were separated by about half the pitch of the rifling in the barrel. Examination of the holes in the sheets revealed ink smudges on the side of each hole but separated from each other by about 180 degrees around the hole. Had the pellet stopped spinning the two smudges would have been at the same angular position on each sheet.

Possibly the most difficult part of testing any gun or pellet in a serious manner is finding somewhere to carry out the test. Ideally a long covered building free from cross drafts is the ideal location, but sheds of that length, or old factory buildings are not very common. We solved the problem on one occasion by buying a long length of polythene sheet which was in fact in the form of a tube. We then permanently sealed off one end of the tube with sticky tape and partially sealed the other so that we could get in and out. Rifles, targets and a pellet stop were placed in the tube before we inflated it with a vacuum cleaner. In this instance the tube inflated to forty feet long and about four feet in diameter, but it offered all the facilities we needed and folded away afterwards for future use. The system has one drawback however, the tube should be placed close to a fence or wall to keep it steady since it is liable to blow about in a strong wind.

Chapter 19
THE PELLET'S FLIGHT

In the chapter on barrels we pointed out that the muzzle is probably the most important part of the whole tube as far as accuracy is concerned, it is at that point that the pellet's course relative to the sight line is dictated. We therefore spent many hours investigating exactly how a pellet behaves at the muzzle; we wanted to know what factors influence it as it leaves to start its flight to the target.

Spark Photography

Our chief tool during these investigations was *"Spark Photography"*. It is a procedure by which a projectile may be photographed in flight; although the picture is a silhouette or shadowgraph rather than a true photograph, it is nevertheless of great value because it shows the pattern of the airflow round the pellet which is the all important factor in airgun ballistics. We were first introduced to this technique by Mr. C.B. Daish during a visit to the Royal Military College of Science at Shrivenham in Wiltshire, since then it has been of immense value to us in the investigation of pellet flight.

The system relies on the instantaneous and very intense light of a high voltage spark freezing the pellet in mid flight. Unexposed high sensitivity film is placed a few inches behind the pellet, the spark source being positioned a few feet in front of it. We used an infra red beam to trigger the spark, the beam being placed slightly in front of the muzzle, or mounted so as to pass through windows fitted into the barrel itself a couple of inches back from the muzzle. We also used an electronic variable delay unit so that the spark could be fired at any chosen time after the pellet had broken the beam. With this system we were able to photograph a pellet at any point of interest during the first part of its journey. The process itself is simple enough, the difficulty arises in handling the equipment because the whole procedure has to carried out in total darkness. To make things a little easier for ourselves we used luminous spots to pin point the more important items, such as the pellets, breech and air valves.

During earlier experiments carried out before writing "The Airgun from Trigger to Muzzle (1976)" we took pictures of pellets as they left the muzzle of our spring powered rifle, these pellets were always followed by an impressive array of shock waves. Yet when we fired darts we found that the air behind them had little or no energy left. We deduced this because the dart's tail remained firmly at its rear, smoothed down and compressed by the airflow as it flew forward. This surprised us because we had assumed that the presence of shock waves indicated a source of energy and expanding air, we therefore expected the tail feathers to be blown forwards. We can only assume that the shock waves are generated at the start of the barrel and continue along it behind the pellet, dispersing slowly as they leave.

When we started photographing pellets fired from a pneumatic for inclusion in the present work we were slightly disappointed to find that the air blast from the muzzle is not as spectacular as those we had seen previously from spring guns. In each case it takes the form of an expanding balloon whose size is only influenced by the magnitude of the air pressure behind the pellet. However, as soon as we photographed darts, especially at high velocity, we saw exactly what we had expected to see, the tails were blown about in a most dramatic manner (**fig. 19.10**). Even at very low velocities the tails were considerably disturbed, while at high velocity they were blown completely sideways. How far down range the tails remain expanded we don't know because we can only photograph them up to about eight inches away from the muzzle; but something like twelve to eighteen inches, depending upon their velocity, would seem to be a probable figure.

One of the more interesting surprises arising from this photography was accidental. We had been told that all projectiles tend to *yaw* as they leave the muzzle, that is they wobble and point in various directions before settling down to their correct path. We had never seen this occur in any of our previous studies, yet many pictures of pellets fired during the early stages of these pneumatic experiments showed pellets tilted and clearly out of line with the barrel (**fig. 19.13**). At first we thought we had stumbled on one of the causes of "flyers" until we examined the muzzle very carefully and found that we were accidentally using a barrel whose muzzle had been opened up for some previous experiment, but what was worse a screw which we had used for stopping the chrono projected slightly into this enlarged section. Here obviously was the reason for the excessive yaw. When we mentioned this to our ballistics expert he pointed out that in fact this system is often used during the development of new military shells. They purposely introduce excessive yaw to give them relative figures as to the performance of the round.

Chapter 19 - The Pellet's Flight

The following are just a few of the dozens of pictures that we have taken over the years. We learned a great many things from these experiments, we were able for the first time to see the airflow around the pellet not only as it emerged from the muzzle but also during the first few inches of its journey. Unfortunately it was not possible to determine the down range accuracy of the shots as this would have required a dark tunnel at least twenty yards long.

fig.19.1

Fig. 19.1: In our early experiments we were very surprised to see bubbles like these appearing at the muzzle. We soon realised that they were in fact the oily exhaust from the previous shot being pushed out ahead of the next shot. Blowing down the barrel before loading cured the problem.

fig.19.2

Fig. 19.2: Darts were an important tool in our investigations because their tails clearly indicate the direction and intensity of the airflow over them. These two pictures of darts fired from spring guns show that they are experiencing little or no pressure behind their tails.

fig.19.3

Fig. 19.3: Here two pellets were loaded together to see whether they stayed together in the barrel of a pneumatic. The balloon of expanding air is characteristic of every shot fired from a pneumatic.

Fig. 19.4: Firing pellets or darts the wrong way round often yields interesting facts about the airflow around them. In this instance the small amount of air leaving the barrel of the spring gun is clearly travelling slightly faster than the dart since it has stripped hairs from the tail and is moving them forward.

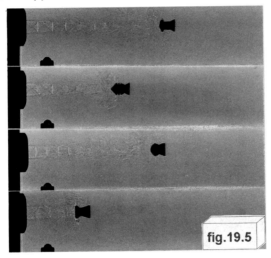

Fig. 19.5: A selection of pellets have been fired backwards, they all show the characteristic shock waves which follow a pellet from the muzzle of a spring gun and also the cloud of low energy air dispersing around the nose of the pellet.

Fig. 19.6, 19.7, 19.8: The progress of three spring driven pellets is traced in these pictures. It is clear that as the pellet advances the airflow and shock waves behind it decay until the pellet is flying without much disturbance to the air around it.

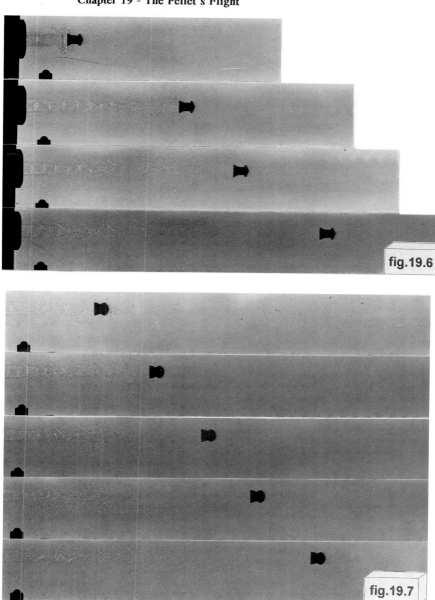

fig.19.6

fig.19.7

The Air Gun from Trigger to Target

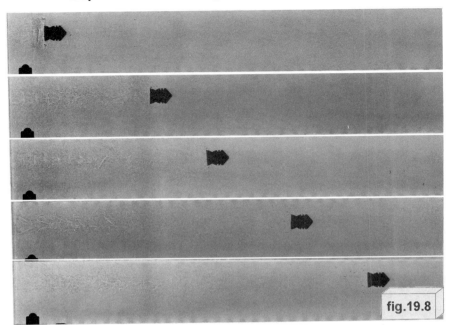

fig.19.8

Fig. 19.9: Eight further spring driven pellets, including a ball. The small vertical object near the muzzle in these pictures is the detector of the infra red beam which is broken by the pellet as it passes.

Fig. 19.10: The enormous energy remaining in the air as it leaves the muzzle of a pneumatic is demonstrated by these darts.

Fig 19.11: These two show that air passed the dart's body as it was driven up the barrel and stripped some loose hairs from its tail and blew them out of the muzzle ahead of the dart. At same time the tail of the dart was expanded by the air ahead of it.

Fig. 19.12: A selection of pellets as they leave the muzzle of a pneumatic.

Fig. 19.13: This series shows pellets leaving a muzzle that has been damaged and are yawing badly. Although this is unacceptable in a normal rifle, the introduction of yaw is a normal procedure in the development of a new missile as its study yields information about the missile's characteristics.

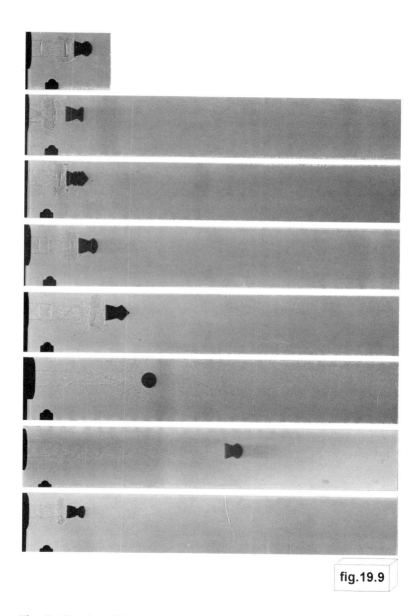

fig.19.9

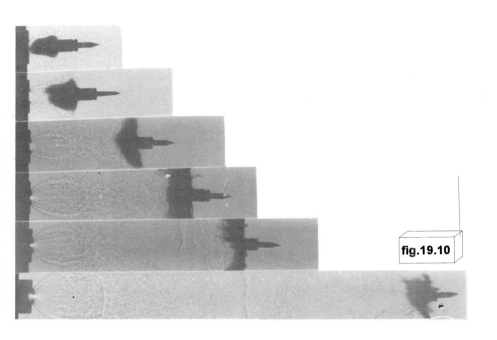

fig.19.10

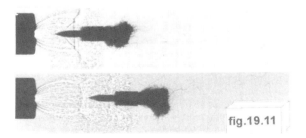

fig.19.11

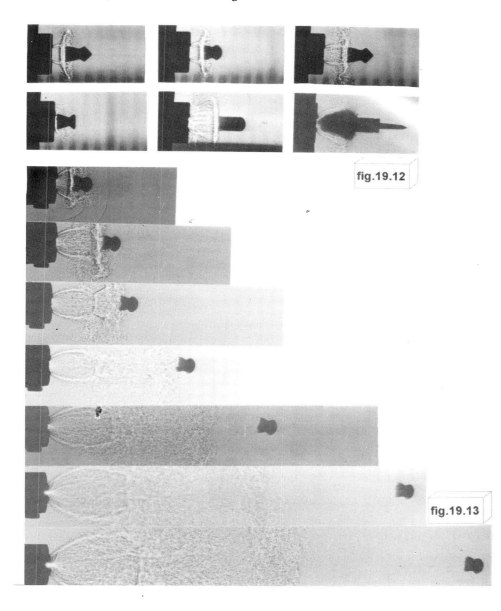

fig.19.12

fig.19.13

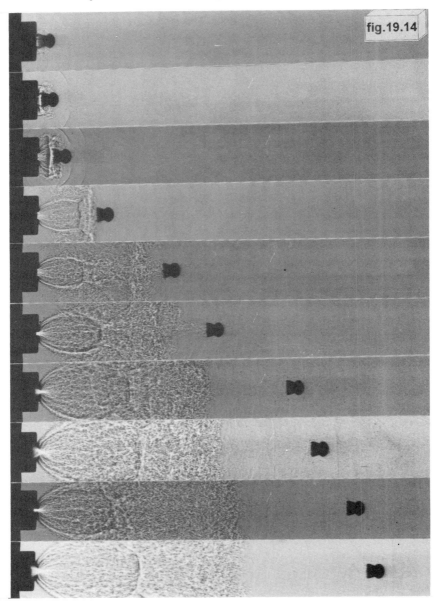

fig.19.14

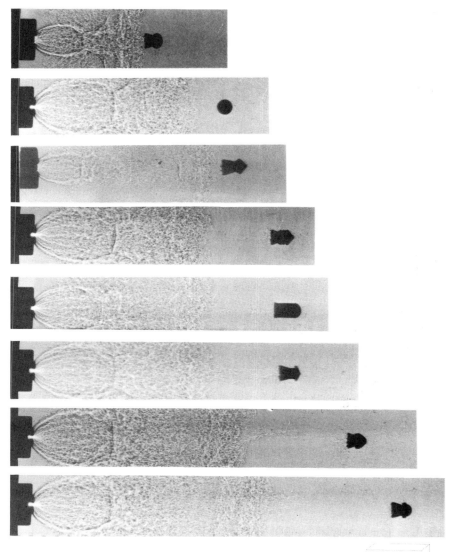

fig.19.15

Fig. 19.14: A series of dome headed pellets as they leave the muzzle and travel down range. The wave seen in front of the first three pellets is in fact the air that travelled up the barrel in front of the pellet.

Fig. 19.15: Another selection of pellets similar to those seen in **fig. 19.9**, but these were fired from a pneumatic.

Theoretical Ballistics

Text books on gunnery, when talking about a trajectory, start off by describing the theoretically perfect curve of a projectile when fired in a vacuum. In that situation a pellet could not lose velocity due to air resistance, it would attain its maximum range when the barrel was set at an elevation of forty five degrees and the pellet would land at the same velocity with which it left the muzzle. Certainly it would lose velocity as it climbed upwards, but it would reagian it all on the return trip. Not many of us are ever likely to put this perfection to the test until an airgunner reserves a ticket to the moon for the pleasure of shooting in a vacuum!

However, here on earth once the pellet leaves the muzzle it becomes subject to our laws of exterior ballistics. Air resistance and gravity being the main headings for these. The earth's gravity causes the pellet to fall at an acceleration rate of 32.2 Ft.per second for every second it is in flight, while at the same time the resistance of the air causes it to slow down. So, as its speed decreases due to air drag it falls further during each succeeding interval of time; also the maximum range is achieved when the barrel is elevated to an angle somewhere between 30 and 35 degrees.

A similar trajectory to that of a pellet may be easily observed in the path taken by the jet from a hose pipe. As the fast flowing water leaves the nozzle it appears to travel in a straight line for a short distance, but as the friction caused by the surrounding air slows it down it falls to earth in a smooth curve.

The rudiments of this complicated science go right back to the beginning of mankind's need to hunt, bows and arrows are a reasonable starting point. Robin Hood had to learn how far to aim above the target to allow for the fall of his arrows, but obviously calculations became more important with the coming of gunpowder. The chief stumbling block to the study of cannon balls was the lack of suitable timing equipment and many odd theories were arrived at to describe their flight. It was thought, at one time, that after leaving the gun they travelled in a straight line then followed a curved path as they changed direction before falling to earth in another straight line.

The mathematical study of exterior ballistics is a bottomless pit, the more you know about it the more there is to know, it can cover everything from our humble pellets, to military shells and then on to the study of space rockets. The deeper one delves into the subject the more complicated the mathematics become. There are few books available on the subject, so anyone wishing to pursue the science further must visit a library and ask them to obtain a work on this specialised subject. In this chapter we will confine ourselves to the sections which have an observable influence on our tiny pellet's flight during the short time and distance it is in the air.

Such subjects as the rotation of the earth, variations in temperature and humidity, as well as barometric pressure may well be taken into account when shooting up to a thousand yards at Bisley but are well outside the sphere of airguns, though we will say something about the *Magnus effect* and wind drift. The problems associated with supersonic velocities will however not be covered.

Pellet Trajectory

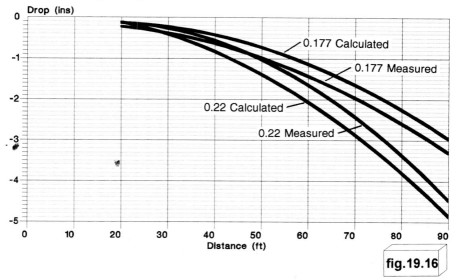

fig.19.16

One of the first subjects for our study was pellet drop. We did a very careful experiment to establish the difference between the theory and practice of pellet fall. We soon found that when fired over a distance of thirty yards .177 pellets dropped about 0.3 of an inch further than calculated while .22 calibre pellets dropped 0.03 of an inch less than expected. They were all fired at velocities of 815 and 590 FPS respectively, that is maintaining a muzzle energy of 12 Ft. Lbs. in each calibre. The curves are shown in **Fig. 19.16**. The exact reason for this anomaly was never found, but it is probable that as the pellet flies the aerodynamics of its shape causes some pellets to experience a small amount of lift as they fly, while others may be forced downwards. This is a phenomenon which effects many other projectiles, so we were not surprised to find it in the flight of a pellet also.

The cause of this difference in the fall of the pellet is not the same as that which makes footballs or tennis balls suddenly rise, dip or swerve in mid flight, that curving results from the spin of the ball and is in fact caused by the *Magnus effect*. The curved flight induced by the *Magnus effect* results from a higher pressure being generated on one side of a spinning object like a tennis ball as it flies through the air. If the ball, as it leaves the player, is spinning about its horizontal axis with its top moving backwards towards the player then the ball will tend to climb because the airflow over its top tends to stay with the surface of the ball creating an area of increased pressure behind and slightly below the ball forcing it upwards. If the ball is rotating about its vertical axis its flight will curve towards the side that is moving back towards the player. Careful observation during a tennis or football match will often reveal this uncanny curve in the ball's flight as it travels to the target. Since our pellets usually spin clockwise about their fore and aft axis, the only drift they can generate is sideways and to the right. All spin stabilized pellets drift in the direction of their spin, however only a very small part of this drift is caused by the *Magnus effect*, the main cause of the drift is the gyroscopic stabilization itself. As the pellet tries to change direction earthwards the gyroscopic action causes it to point slightly to the right which produces a lift force pointing to the right. The rate of drift increases further down range because the longer the drift force acts on the pellet the faster it is moving to the right and hence the larger the drift.

We carried out several checks on the setting up of the equipment just in case the extra lift or fall was being caused by an apparatus error, the chief suspect was the height of the target relative to the muzzle because it is not easy to position two points accurately when they are thirty yards apart. We solved this problem by using a translucent hose pipe filled with coloured water.

Chapter 19 - The Pellet's Flight

Provided there are no large bubbles in it, each end surface of the water in the pipe must be at the same level, thus we can use these two points to set up the rifle and target at exactly the same level.

The obvious gun to be used during this experiment was our *projector*. We first checked that the barrel was mounted dead straight and level, but even setting a barrel correctly by use of an engineer's spirit level is no guarantee that it will shoot level, it may have internal faults which throw the pellet off course. We overcame this difficulty by a process that came to be known as *"shooting the barrel round"*. This involved rotating the barrel within the projector's mounting rings and firing shots at about thirty degree intervals so as to establish exactly where each pellet printed on the target sheet. Some barrels were capable of producing a smaller circle of prints than others, very few give a tight ragged hole. Once a full circle of prints had been established, the barrel could be positioned so that the shots landed in either the 9 or 3 o'clock position, in other words the barrel was shooting either left or right, but not up or down. In this experiment, where we were examining only the pellet's drop, the fact that the shots were going left or right was of no consequence.

We used a chrono to measure the total time of flight and then calculated the theoretical drop (D) based on that time, using the equation:

$$D = 1/2gt^2 \times 12.$$

Where g is 32.2, t is in seconds and D in inches.

(This may be simplified into multiplying the time of flight by itself and then by 193.2).

Notice that there has been no mention of the pellet's weight, this is because weight, or more correctly "mass", is of no importance of determining drop. A heavy body falls at exactly the same rate of acceleration as a light one, 32.2 Ft. per second per second, commonly known as g. In other words after the first second of its fall it will have accelerated downwards to a velocity of 32.2 FPS, after the next second it will have further accelerated to 64.4 FPS, and so on. Sir Isaac Newton reassured himself on this point by dropping objects from the dome of St. Paul's Cathedral. It must be remembered that g is an acceleration not a distance. If one asks the question, how far will an object fall in one second and then uses the above equation to calculate the answer, one realises that the distance is 193.2 inches, or 16 feet, not 32.2 feet.

A brief diversion, we sometimes speak of weight and sometimes of mass. If a communications satellite weighing one ton here on earth is taken up to its orbit in space it becomes 'weightless'. This is because its velocity in orbit around the earth generates enough centrifugal force to exactly counterbalance the pull of the earth's gravity; the satellite has obviously not lost any of its mass. It may therefore be said that mass is what is left of a body after the pull of gravity has been removed.

Looking at acceleration in terms of a motor car. Its capability to increase speed depends on two factors, the engine's power and the total weight of the vehicle. A powerful engine in a light body will offer a high rate of acceleration, conversely a low powered engine in a heavy body will result in poor acceleration. In the case of a falling body, gravity provides the motive power and has a greater attractive force on heavy bodies than light ones. One might therefore expect heavy bodies to fall faster than light ones, but this is not the case because heavy bodies, by virtue of their greater mass are accelerated more slowly than light ones. These two contradicting factors, the increased attraction and the diminished acceleration cancel each other out resulting in the constant value g for all bodies whatever their weight.

It must be realised however that the basic value of g is determined by the fall of an object in a vacuum and it also varies very slightly in different areas of the world. Nevertheless the difference in acceleration between a pellet dropped in a vacuum and one dropped in air, anywhere on the earth, is so small over the velocities with which we are concerned that it must be ignored. However if one considers a parachutist or a feather the situation is very different, here air resistance becomes the major factor, reducing the rate of acceleration considerably, because the surface area is so large relative the its weight.

From the previous equation it is clear that the only factor influencing the drop of a pellet is the time (t) during which it is in flight. This time is of course controlled by two factors, the muzzle velocity and the drag which the air exerts on the pellet slowing it down throughout its flight. It is the influence of these two factors which encourage rifle and ammunition makers to seek higher velocities and projectiles with reduced drag. The quicker the pellet can reach its target the less time it will have in which to fall, therefore the curve of the trajectory will be reduced. This in turn will simplify the alteration of the sights to compensate for increased ranges.

We based our calculation for the pellet's drop (**Fig. 19.16**) solely on the time taken for it to travel between the muzzle and a target set thirty yards away, a reasonable distance for an airgun. We assumed that the pellet travelled in a straight line between the two points, although we know that in fact it followed the slightly longer path of its curved trajectory. In this situation the difference between the two distances is negligible. But we must make the point that as the range increases, and therefore the necessary elevation of the muzzle, (possibly beyond a point which is acceptable for shooting with an air rifle) the trajectory will become so pronounced that the flight distance, and therefore its time, will be increased considerably. If we were to allow for a curved trajectory the calculation of the drop would become very complicated indeed and well outside the sphere of airgun ballistics.

The control of muzzle velocity has already been discussed in the earlier chapters, so we must now concentrate on the drag which slows the pellet down after it has left the muzzle and how it effects the flight time. This is important because once the time of flight of a projectile to any point along its trajectory is known, its velocity at that spot can also be calculated. Therefore its velocity loss, or retardation, over short intervals of the total distance may also be found. It must however, be borne in mind when dealing with a pellet in flight that it is not being slowed down at a constant rate, the greater the velocity the greater the retardation. When the pellet's velocity has fallen by half, the air resistance to its progress has been reduced to a quarter. This situation is called a square law.

The square law is not a difficult concept to understand if one looks at the situation the other way round. If we wish to double the velocity of a pellet, we must be prepared to increase the input energy four times. This is because the resistance applied by the air to any moving object increases four times when the velocity is doubled *(see Chapter 1)*. There is a limit to this straight forward increase in resistance, depending slightly on the shape of the pellet, it will occur at about 700 FPS upwards. In the instance of a dome headed pellet the air must move faster as it flows over the blunt dome and its speed may therefore become close to the speed of sound at that point, therefore the total resistance must also increase steeply. From this it is obvious that any figure used to describe the resistance of the air to a pellet's flight can only be perfectly correct at one particular velocity.

The speed of sound in the atmosphere at the standard temperature and pressure, is 1,116.5 FPS (usually quoted as 1,100 FPS) but the air resistance rises steeply above this figure and other laws apply. Since most airguns produce velocities below the speed of sound we will confine our calculations to sub sonics.

Each different calibre, pellet shape, or velocity will alter the retardation characteristics of a pellet and in the very practical world of airguns such terms as *"Ballistic Coefficient"* or *"Ballistic Tables"* have very little relevance because we normally set our rifle's sights by trial and error to suit a particular pellet. Also, we learn from experience by how much we should alter our sights or aim above the target to allow for the pellet's fall as the range increases. The majority of pellets have similar ballistic characteristics in each calibre, therefore at acceptable airgun ranges, only a small alteration to the sight is necessary to accommodate the difference when the brand or shape of the pellet is changed.

Generally the cost of our pellets is negligible and we are therefore perfectly happy to expend as many shots as necessary when adjusting our sights. We would not normally consider sitting down with a calculator to work out the sight setting for a target a certain distance away, even if we had enough information about the pellet's ballistic characteristics to do so in the first place. Also, the calculation would require an accurate range finding facility, which although perfectly possible with a modern scope, it is not likely to be employed in the field as part of a calculated trajectory when the target is a rabbit.

On the other hand the situation with an artillery shell is totally different, the cost of one shell probably exceeds that of our best rifle, it is also very important that the first shell lands on, or as close as possible to the target. In the field of naval gunnery theoretical ballistics becomes even more important, especially when the target is out of sight over the horizon. Few of their equations are applicable to our tiny pellets, their calculations concern supersonic flight, also allowances for the earth's rotation must be made for the time the shell is in flight, a factor unlikely to trouble us very much.

Although we have indicated that the theory of ballistics has little place in the field of airguns we feel that this fascinating subject is well worth description. Future pellets may have characteristics so different to those available at present that an understanding of the terms used in ballistics may be the only way by which accurate comparisons will be possible.

Over the years we have seen articles in which *Ballistic Tables* and *Ballistic Coefficients* have been discussed, yet when we tried to translate these into useful information about the flight of a pellet we found there were flaws in the argument. Text books often cover the subject in too much depth, bringing in details and problems which have no place in airgunning. We finally abandoned our efforts to unravel the tangle and asked our friend Miles Morris to help us to sort out the important facts for us.

The most common term used when describing the performance of a projectile is its *"Ballistic Coefficient"* C. We have all come across this term and no doubt imagined that if only we could fully understand its meaning we would be able to solve all our accuracy problems. This would be far from the truth, firstly because C has nothing to do with accuracy as such, it is mainly a term which compares the performance of a projectile with that of a "standard shell" whose behaviour and characteristics have been studied in great detail.

However, within the context of airguns C is not the best coefficient to use because it embodies corrections for atmospheric conditions, these, as we have already pointed out are of no interest to us at all. We will therefore use the term CO which is better suited to our application.

The first equation we should look at when we are considering the theoretical and scientific study of a pellet's passage through the air is the one which determines its *sectional density*. The sectional density describes the pellet's fundamental characteristic relative to the air. It is the ratio of the pellet's mass to its diameter.

$$\text{Sectional Density} = \frac{W}{d^2}$$

Where   W = the weight of the pellet in pounds.
        d = the diameter of the pellet in inches.

For a first example we will look at a light weight .22 pellet weighing 12 grains, not forgetting that there are 7,000 grains in a pound, so 12 must be divided by 7,000 to give 0.001714 of a pound. Also that $0.22^2 = 0.0484$

Thus Sectional Density $= \dfrac{0.001714}{0.0484} = 0.03595$

Suppose we look now at another .22 pellet, but this one weighs 20 grains.

Sectional Density $= \dfrac{0.002875}{0.0484} = 0.05903$

These figure then are the sectional densities of the pellets, although the mass is in pounds and the diameter in inches these units are not normally quoted. It is only the ratio which is useful to us and enables us to continue our calculations.

All other things being equal the second of the two pellets should go further for the same muzzle velocity, because being heavier it will have stored more energy. But suppose the first pellet had a far better aerodynamic shape than the second, then our simple comparison is not correct, we must look further and allow for the difference in drag.

The same simple equation with the addition of the *form factor i* takes us to the basic equation for determining the *Ballistic Coefficient CO*. We don't have to concern ourselves directly with the value of the form factor of the pellet we are using because it is already included in the coefficient *CO*.

$$CO = \frac{W}{i\ d^2}$$

The letter *i* is the *form factor*, or shape and steadiness factor for the particular pellet being used, it is a very important item and has a large effect on the final figure, especially at high velocities. As we have already seen in the previous chapter there is a large difference between the drag on a flat headed pellet and one with a round or pointed head. The value of the form factor alters with velocity, so unless the pellet's flight characteristics are known there is no further we can go with the calculation.

It is not too difficult to arrive at the values of *CO* and *i* if we have a chrono, or better still two chronos with which we can measure the velocity of every pellet at two points along its flight path. If only one chrono is available then an accurate average of velocities at each position must be established, the number of shots fired to obtain this figure is a matter of experience with the rifle and pellet in question, but it is advisable to ignore any very high or very low readings so that the figure used represents a consistent average.

Ballistic Tables

The *Ballistic Tables* shown on the following page are reproduced from the from the original 1928 Ballistic Tables, whose formulation is beyond the scope of this present work.

We can use these to determine various characteristics of the pellet's flight: Suppose the muzzle velocity of a 10 grain .177 pellet is 700 FPS and the velocity at a point 90 feet away is 600 FPS. We can using the tables determine the *ballistic coefficient CO:*

V_1 = 700 FPS Muzzle Velocity   From the table *(S):* S_1 = 48932.3
V2 = 600 FPS at D = 90ft   From the table *(S):* S_2 = 44937.2

Subtracting $(S_1 - S_2)$ = 3995.1

Now $CO = \dfrac{D}{(S_1 - S_2)} = \dfrac{90}{3995.1} = 0.0225$

Thus under these conditions $CO = $ **0.0225**

However if we now wish to know the value of i, the form factor, we can use the previous equation thus:

$$i = \frac{\text{Sectional Density}}{CO} = \frac{W/d^2}{CO} = \frac{0.0456}{0.0225} = 2.027$$

The tables may be used in the following manner to determine the velocity at any point down range as long as its *CO* and muzzle velocity are known. Suppose we wish to know the velocity of the same pellet at 60 Ft. when its muzzle velocity is 700 FPS and its *CO* 0.0225.

From previous: $(S_1 - S_2) = \dfrac{D}{CO} = \dfrac{60}{0.0225} = 2666.7$

Now looking up the value of S (S_1) in the table at 700 FPS: = 48932.3

V vel. (FPS)	T	S dist. (Feet)	V vel. (FPS)	T	S dist. (Feet)
400	177.26	34645.2	770	207.946	51420.4
410	178.78	35260.8	780	208.382	51758.3
420	180.23	35862.6	790	208.807	52091.9
430	181.62	36453.3	800	209.222	52421.8
440	182.95	37031.8	810	209.627	52747.8
450	184.22	37957.0	820	210.023	53070.5
460	185.44	38152.1	830	210.410	53389.8
470	186.61	38696.1	840	210.788	53705.4
480	187.73	39228.1	850	211.155	54015.5
490	188.81	39751.9	860	211.508	54317.3
500	189.85	40266.7	870	211.847	54610.5
510	190.847	40770.2	880	212.173	54895.8
520	191.806	41264.1	890	212.487	55173.7
530	192.731	41749.7	900	212.789	55444.0
540	193.625	42228.0	910	213.079	55706.5
550	194.489	42698.9	920	213.359	55962.7
560	195.323	43161.8	930	213.629	56212.5
570	196.127	43616.1	940	213.890	56456.5
580	196.905	44063.5	950	214.142	56694.6
590	197.658	44504.6	960	214.38	56927.6
600	198.386	44937.2	970	214.622	57155.3
610	199.091	45363.7	980	214.850	57377.6
620	199.774	45783.7	990	215.070	57594.3
630	200.437	46198.6	1000	215.282	57805.2
640	201.080	46606.4	1010	215.487	58011.2
650	201.703	47008.2	1020	215.686	58213.2
660	202.308	47404.5	1030	215.880	58412.1
670	202.895	47794.8	1040	216.070	58608.7
680	203.465	48179.6	1050	216.252	58798.9
690	204.018	48558.4	1060	216.424	58980.4
700	204.556	48932.3	1070	216.586	59152.9
710	205.080	49301.7	1080	216.739	59317.4
720	205.590	49666.4	1090	216.884	59474.7
730	206.086	50026.0	1100	217.021	59624.7
740	206.569	50381.0	1110	217.151	59768.3
750	204.040	50731.9	1120	217.274	59905.4
760	207.499	51078.4	1130	217.390	60035.9

Now: $S_2 = S_1 - 2666.7 = 46265.6$

From the tables the nearest value of S to this is 46198.1 or 46606.4, taking for simplicity the 46198.1 value since that is the nearer of the two. A velocity of 630 FPS appears in the corresponding first column. This then is the velocity of the pellet 60 Ft. (20 yards) away from the rifle.

If we had wanted to know the time of flight to the point 60 Ft. away we would go back to the tables and look at the value of T when V equals 630 FPS. A value of 200.437 is shown. At the same time we must look up the value of T when V is 700 FPS, this is 204.556.

Now: $T_1 - T_2 = 4.119$

Time of flight $t = T \times CO = 0.0927$ seconds.

If we had wanted to do the above calculation more accurately, then we should find the exact value for the velocity at $S = 46265.6$ by proportion from the two figures either side. In this case the value of V would have come to 631.7 FPS and the value of T would be 200.543 giving a time of flight of 0.0903 seconds.

As a check on the above calculations, we used figures obtained during earlier experiments, in that instance a .22 pellet was used. The muzzle velocity was 590 FPS and the velocity at 90 feet was 519 FPS. These figures gave us a CO value of 0.02777. Using this value of CO we calculated the velocity to be 550 FPS at 50 feet, whereas the observed velocity at this distance was 549 FPS. The calculated time of flight over distance was 0.088 seconds, while the observed time of flight was 0.083 seconds. In other words the predicted values were the same as those observed in practice.

Repeating the calculation for determining CO but this time over a distance of 20 feet with the same muzzle velocity of 590 FPS and a final velocity 587 FPS, the value of CO changed slightly to 0.1510. This difference demonstrates that the value of CO, in the case of an airgun pellet, changes slightly depending upon the velocity or how much of the trajectory is used as a basis for its calculation. From this it is clear that when establishing the CO of a certain pellet it is well worth going to the trouble of obtaining figures representative of the velocity and distance over which the pellet is likely to be fired. In the case of a bullet which has considerably less drag the same value of Ballistic Coefficient is acceptable through out a large span of velocities and ranges.

Using the above figures and the earlier equation for drop, the fall of the pellet may be calculated for each of a number of points along the pellet's flight path. From these drop figures it is not difficult to construct the curve followed by the pellet as it flies, also the maximum reasonable range for that pellet. Obviously the barrel of the rifle will have to be tilted up slightly to allow for the pellet's fall, thus increasing its flight distance, but this will be ignored in our calculations because the difference between the actual distance and that followed by an airgun pellet is small. The greater the distance to the target the greater the elevation of the barrel will have to be to compensate for the increased flight time and therefore pellet drop.

We carried out the calculations for the pellet we mentioned earlier whose CO was 0.02777 to give us the following drop values.

Dist.Ft.	20	30	40	50	60	70	80	90
Drop.Ins.	.25	.50	.92	1.47	2.21	3.57	4.28	5.13

It must be admitted that this was a long and patience defying task. First the velocity at each point had to be calculated, then the flight time to that point and finally the drop produced by the flight time. Of course we used a calculator, but as we worked we remembered the early ballisticians who before 1890 produced the tables, also the gunners who had to use them prior to the age of computers.

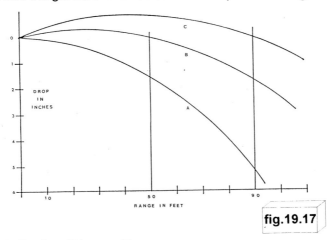

fig.19.17

From the above drop figures we drew three curves. **(Fig. 19.17)** Curve **A** is drawn exactly from the listed figures and shows the pellet's trajectory when it is fired from a rifle whose barrel is held horizontally, this is the simplest way to initially visualise the curve. However, in practice we need to know what the curve looks like at certain distances from the muzzle so that we can compare different types of pellet. This is not difficult to achieve because all we need to do is bend a piece of soft wire to the shape of the curve and then swing it up pivoting it about the point which represents the muzzle. When the wire crosses a vertical line relative to the distance we are shooting at we can now see the curved path of the pellet relative to that point, this is illustrated by curves **B** and **C** which are drawn for ranges of 50 and 90 feet respectively. We can also see what happens to that pellet both before and beyond the point at which we zeroed the rifle. This system is perfectly adequate for airgunners shooting at normal distances and at reasonable elevations or depressions of the barrel, but if the target is very much higher or lower relative to the gun we have to make a reduced allowance which must be based on experience.

If one wishes to know the acceptable maximum range for the rifle and pellet combination it is not difficult to continue calculations further down range, well beyond the 30 yards where we have stopped. From these figures we can see the shape of the trajectory at these distances and decide whether shooting at such ranges is practical.

Some years ago an enthusiast carried out a detailed experiment and found that .22 pellets could travel slightly over 300 yards, while .177 fell somewhat short of this range. Each calibre was fired at an energy of 12 Ft. Lbs. However at these distances the muzzle had to be raised to unusable elevations and of course the pellets fell over a very wide area.

A difficulty now arises as far as the airgunner is concerned, the only way in which a barrel can be preset to guarantee the pellet will arrive correctly on the target is by measuring the angle through which it is tilted relative to the ground. Measuring this angle is the procedure used when setting up an artillery piece, but it is of no practical help in our sphere of ballistics, we have no convenient means of measuring angles. However as long as we know that our rifle is correctly zeroed at a certain range we can see from the curve how much "hold over" or "hold under" must be applied to hit a target at a different range.

It has been said that, "calculations are an idealised system of analysis." This seems to be a very true statement when dealing with an airgun trajectory.

It is very easy to get seduced into using three or four places of decimals on a pocket calculator or computer, yet common sense tells us that in practice no two pellets ever land that close to one another, and in any case one can't measure a pellet's position to a thousandth of an inch. Neither must we forget that the original pellet's characteristics will have been based on the average of a number of shots, so the figures must be viewed with a certain amount of uncertainty. This uncertainty factor is further compounded by having to ignore other small elements such as a pellet's possible aerodynamic lift. This all brings us back to the earlier statement that an understanding of a *ballistic coefficient* is not a guarantee of successful shooting, but it does perhaps help in understanding why we miss.

It might not be out of place here to define the *ballistic coefficient* thus: It is a multiplier expressing the relationship of the standard drag function to the actual. Or in other words, the ratio of the former to the latter. The standard drag function being that of a known projectile whose performance in flight has been studied in great detail. However, in our case we are having to compare the characteristics of our pellets with those of a military shell because ballistic tables were developed using a small shell as the "standard" round.

The use of the ballistic coefficient as the basis for the study of projectiles has, in recent years, been largely replaced by the term *"Drag Coefficient"*. *Cd*. This figure takes advantage of the ease with which we can now measure velocity, also the value of *Cd* relates to the particular projectile or pellet in question and is not a 'comparison' relating it to a standard. It is therefore a figure which represents the pellet's flight characteristics more accurately than *CO*.

$$Cd = \frac{M}{K\,S}\, Ln\left(\frac{V_1}{V_2}\right)$$

M = Weight of pellet in grains.
V_1 = Muzzle velocity. FPS.
V_2 = Velocity at target. FPS.
K = A Constant.
S = Range in yards.

K for: .177 = 0.1374,   .20 = 0.17514,
         .22 = 0.20529,   .25 = 0.27365.

Taking figures from actual shooting experiments we found that for a typical .177 round headed pellet flying at 750 FPS over 30 yds. *Cd* is 0.590 and that for a similar shaped .22 pellet flying at 770 FPS over 30 yds. *Cd* is 0.480. When calculating and comparing the *Cd* values for different pellets the velocity and distance in each case must be the same. A low value of *Cd* indicates a low value of drag on that pellet.

In the previous chapter we measured the drag of a pellet in the wind tunnel, the figures we obtained, in grains, may now be directly converted to give the *Cd* of the pellet at the velocity of the air over the pellet while in the tunnel which was about 130 FPS. The drag force exerted on the pellet must be divided by a factor which depends on its calibre these are:

.177 is 24.01,   .20 is 30.6,   .22 is 35.87,   .25 is 47.81

Thus for the case of the typical .177 the force on the pellet was 12 grains so after dividing this by 24.01 a *Cd* of 0.499 is produced. In the case of the .22 a *Cd* of 0.348 is produced after dividing the force of 12.5 grains by 35.87.

Knowing *Cd* it is possible to calculate the time of flight using the following equation.

$$t = \frac{3M}{K\,Cd} \left(\frac{1}{V_2} - \frac{1}{V_1} \right)$$

It is also possible to calculate the time of flight if *Cd* is unknown, by using.

$$t = \frac{3S \left(\dfrac{1}{V_2} - \dfrac{1}{V_1} \right)}{Ln\ (V_1/V_2)}$$

M is the weight of the pellet in grains, S is the distance in yards and K is the constant used in the earlier equation.

One of the most difficult skills to learn in airgunning is how much allowance to make when shooting on a windy day. This subject is made even more difficult because the wind seldom blows steadily from one direction, but there is an equation which may be of help. It is called the Rifleman's Formula.

$$D = W(T - T_2)$$

$D =$ Deflection of pellet in feet.
$W =$ Wind velocity in FPS straight across the trajectory.
$T =$ Time of pellet's flight to target.
$T_2 =$ The time it would take for the pellet to cover the same distance in a vacuum. The pellet would then travel the whole distance at its muzzle velocity.

Suppose a pellet leaves the muzzle at 600 FPS and travels 90 Ft. (30 Yds.) to the target, but there is a crosswind of 1 Mile per Hour blowing. (1 MPH equals 1.4667 FPS) Using the tables it can be found that the time of flight for the pellet would be about 0.165 second in the air, in a vacuum it would be .150 secs. The deflection caused by the wind would be .022 feet, or 0.264 inches.

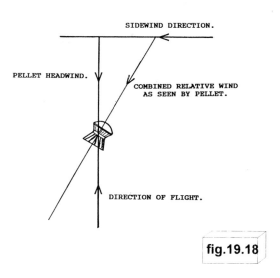

SIDEWIND DIRECTION.

PELLET HEADWIND.

COMBINED RELATIVE WIND AS SEEN BY PELLET.

DIRECTION OF FLIGHT.

fig.19.18

This is a somewhat theoretical way out of a difficult situation since it assumes that the wind is blowing consistently and the marksman knows all about his pellet's ballistics.

The small sketch **(fig.19.18)** shows, in an exaggerated manner, how a pellet reacts to a side wind blowing from the right, it is clear that the pellet has turned slightly to its right as it flies. It has turned to face what it sees as its head wind, this wind is the combination of the air flowing over it as it travels forward as well as that coming from its right. The drag of the pellet now acts in the direction of the relative wind and is therefore at an angle to the direction of the pellet's flight. It is this drag force acting at an angle to the pellet's true flight direction which causes the pellet to drift down wind. The marksman must therefore allow for this drift by aiming slightly to the right of the target. If the pellet had no drag at all it would turn to face the relative wind but would continue with its original flight path. This is the situation which applies to rockets while their "sustainer motor" is running, this motor produces just enough thrust to eliminate the drag. However, while the main motor is burning and there is more thrust than drag the rocket will drift into the wind, but as soon as this motor goes out the rocket will start to drift down wind like any other projectile.

Chapter 19 - The Pellet's Flight

Chapter 20
ACCURACY

Up until now the accuracy of shots has not been discussed in detail, because hard experience has impressed on us that one must know a great deal about the peculiarities of airguns and their pellets before a critical study of their accuracy is a worthwhile project. Although we must admit that at the outset of our investigations we spent many happy hours one Summer (1972) shooting in a farmer's field in the hope of unravelling the mysteries of accuracy.

It could be argued that one of the most important characteristics of any rifle is consistency of velocity, this quality, although very significant, may be shown by calculation, not to be quite so critical. We all expect that the velocity of a good rifle won't vary by more than a few feet per second, but if we take an extreme case and calculate the drop of two consecutive pellets whose muzzle velocities are separated by 20 FPS we find that the difference in the point of impact will be found to be very small indeed.

The difference in height may be calculated by referring to the previous chapter. A 0.177 pellet whose muzzle velocity is 700 FPS and whose CO is 0.0225 takes 0.0903 seconds to travel 60 feet. If the same calculation is carried out again for the same pellet, but this time with a muzzle velocity of only 680 FPS it will take 0.0906 secs to reach the same target. If we use both these flight time values to calculate the drop distance for the two velocities, we find that the first pellet fell 1.57 inches during its flight while the second slower one fell 1.58 inches. A difference of only ten thousandths of an inch ! Twenty feet per second difference between two consecutive shots from a modern rifle is very inconsistent indeed, yet even at that wide variation the two points of impact calculate to a tiny fraction of an inch at 20 yards. That is by calculation, and we already know that calculations in airgunning can be suspect.

We have always been painfully aware throughout our previous experiments that our groups tended to be much larger than calculations would indicate. They were also larger than skilled airgunners could produce. We were also aware, not only from our own work, but from discussions with other enthusiasts too, that although some brands of pellet had a greater accuracy capability than others, they did not always live up to their capability in each and every rifle. This has lead to the piece of advice handed out to newcomers by experienced airgunners when they ask about suitable ammunition: "Try as many brands of pellet as you can, then settle on the type which you find to be the most satisfactory in your rifle". This we have always felt is a very negative statement to make, and likely to put off any newcomer to the sport; surely it should be possible to tell a newcomer which type of pellet will be the most accurate in his gun on the day he buys it.

Obviously there were accuracy factors of which we were not aware, so we decided on a very practical approach; but as we debated our strategy we realised that many months would pass before a conclusion might be realised. Nevertheless a long and patience defying study was embarked upon and about 2,000 shots would have to be fired in two calibres before it was complete.

Three barrels in .177 were selected and four in .22. At the same time six different types of .177 pellets were selected and four in .22. We again used the projector to fire the shots so that we could take advantage of its solid mounting and variable power capability. Each barrel/pellet combination was tested at five pressure settings increasing in increments of 200 PSI. The .22 series starting at 200 PSI and the .177 at 400 PSI. In each series these pressures produced velocities encompassing figures which would give powers in the region of 12 Ft.Lbs. of muzzle energy.

The distance in every case was thirty yards, and each pellet was treated in the same manner, that is it was taken from the tin and lightly lubricated with ordinary engine oil before being pushed a quarter of an inch into the breech, and therefore the rifling, ready for firing. Every shot was monitored by a chrono and any which fell well above or below the average velocity were ignored, as also were any which turned out to be flyers, that is landing well away from the main group. We bought a second hand security TV camera and monitor to view the target from the firing point. This relatively small investment saved hours of walking to the target, while at the same time made the job more pleasurable, especially in bad weather.

As the experiment progressed it became very clear that velocity played a large part in the size of the group, but without any definite law. In some combinations of pellets and barrel, a group would start off small at the lowest velocity then steadily open out as the velocity increased, others would do the exact opposite becoming smaller as the velocity increased. In one or two combinations the group would decrease to a minimum during the first two pressure settings, then open out again during the final two.

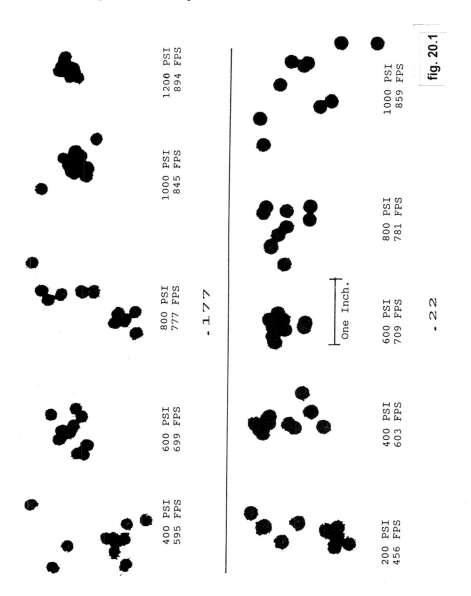

fig. 20.1

1200 PSI
894 FPS

1000 PSI
845 FPS

800 PSI
777 FPS

600 PSI
699 FPS

400 PSI
595 FPS

.177

1000 PSI
859 FPS

800 PSI
781 FPS

600 PSI
709 FPS

400 PSI
603 FPS

200 PSI
456 FPS

.22

One Inch.

The Air Gun from Trigger to Target

Fig 20.1. shows how the group size altered depending on the velocity, in the case of the .177 the group size is smallest at the highest velocity. On the other hand the .22 reduces to minimum and then opens up again. The smallest group in the whole series could easily be covered by a half inch circle, the largest scatter needed a three inch circle to include all the pellet holes.

As we steadily worked our way through all the possible combinations and the results were slowly appearing, we became concerned that our solidly mounted barrels were not giving results as good as those being claimed by individual marksmen shooting off hand. So, as an indication of what might happen if our barrel were mounted in a stock and fired from the shoulder, we again used the rubber mountings that we mentioned in chapter nine when we were discussing barrel vibration. The resiliently mounted barrel immediately reduced the size of the group from half an inch to about three eighths of an inch, but even this does not match the group sizes claimed by experts in off hand shooting.

This raises the interesting question of why a solidly clamped barrel does not produce groups as close as those of a skilled marksman. It is surprising but experience has shown, contrary to expectations, a pneumatic powered rifle barrel clamped very firmly does not necessarily produce groups as close, if not closer, than those obtained by conventional shooting.

However, it is clear from our extensive experiment that the groups obtainable from any rifle fired from the shoulder must also alter in their size depending on the combination of barrel, pellet and power. From this it follows that the advice, "Try as many brands of pellet as possible" is good advice.

Chapter 21
THE MEASUREMENT OF VELOCITY

The measurement of a projectile's velocity is of the utmost importance to the study of external ballistics, also to the development of any new pellet. The chrono is as essential to the ballistician as the speedometer is to the motor car enthusiast, without it he can make little progress or gain factual information from his experiments.

Positive figures for velocity could not be established until Benjamin Robins (1707-1751) invented the Ballistic Pendulum. His purely mechanical system relied for its accuracy on Newton's third law of motion, which states, "Every action on a body produces an equal and opposite reaction." This means that every time his heavy pendulum was struck by a lightweight projectile it swung back with the same momentum as the projectile contained before it hit. In other words the law of the "Conservation of Momentum" was upheld, therefore as long as the weights of the projectile and the pendulum were known, the velocity of the projectile could be calculated from the distance through which the pendulum lifted as it was driven back. Some years ago we developed a miniature version of this pendulum (**fig. 21.1**) scaled down for use with air rifles, the design and mathematics of this instrument were described in detail in our previous book *"The Air Gun from Trigger to Muzzle"* In all probability our pendulum was far more accurate in its scaled down version than the original monster which was used to measure the velocity of cannon balls. Of course we had the huge advantage of calibration from an electronic chrono.

About the beginning of the present century an alternative device was developed by Boulangé, again it was a mechanical system but electrically controlled. At the start of its journey the projectile broke a wire grid carrying an electric current which allowed a long weight to fall as the bullet passed, at the far end of its flight another grid was broken causing a knife to mark the falling weight at a point indicating the distance through which it had dropped. The time of the projectile's flight could then be calculated from the position of the mark on the weight. With the coming of electronics; first valves and then the transistor, the timing of the flight of our tiny pellets has become a fairly simple matter. The modern chrono now costs less than a good rifle and is as accurate as any to be found in professional establishments, an amazing reversal of the situation that existed only a generation ago.

Chapter 21 - The Measurement of Velocity

Throughout this work, when speaking of velocity measurement we have usually used the word chrono; the shortened name follows in much the same direction as we airgunners speak of a scope when we really mean a telescopic sight; it is also a far more convenient name in both writing and conversation. Many books use the word chronograph, or chronoscope, when the correct name should be chronometer. All these long names have been derived from the Greek where: *Chronos, Graphein, Skopein and Metron* all mean, respectively: time, to write, to see and to measure. Inevitably the only correct combination of these words must be "Time" and "to measure". No modern instrument either writes or sees time. So we feel that although the correct word is undoubtedly chronometer, the shortened version "chrono" is perfectly acceptable in modern terminology.

fig. 21.1

The system whereby the velocity of a pellet is measured is much the same as that used during an athletics meeting. Light beams are set up at a carefully measured distance apart, as the athlete breaks the first beam an electronic clock starts counting, then as the second beam is interrupted the clock is stopped. In athletics the clock is only required to display hundredths of a second, but in our case we must be able to read millionths. In other words our time base must run at a far higher rate, partly because we are dealing with an object that is travelling faster, but mainly because our start and stop beams are usually placed much closer together, often just a few inches apart to accommodate the instrument inside a small unit.

When speaking of athletics we use terms such as, "100 yards in 10 seconds, whereas in shooting we talk in terms of "Feet per second" (FPS). At athletics meetings the competitor's performance is never converted to velocity figures such as 30 FPS, that would be meaningless because in athletics we want to know how far the competitor ran in the measured time. From this information we could calculate, if necessary, his average velocity over the course. In shooting we seldom need to know the average velocity or how far the shot went, its velocity at the start of its journey is the important figure. Also, in shooting, our light beams are positioned very close together so that we can obtain an almost instantaneous velocity reading.

Generally speaking there are two types of chrono, though they both use the system we have just described. The first and more popular is a self contained unit which houses two sets of multiple light beams, normally infra-red. The beams are placed about six inches apart inside a square metal tube, the pellet is then fired through the tube from a short distance away. This short distance allows any smoke or air disturbance to be dissipated before it is enters the tube where it might produce an incorrect reading. The second system is similar to the first but in this case it relies on the interruption of daylight falling on two small photosensitive electronic units called Sky Screens. The sky screens are separate units which may be placed at any convenient distance apart; although they are usually employed outdoors and operated by daylight they may also be used indoors under artificial lights.

Each of the two systems has its strengths and weaknesses; in the first instance, since the beams are always set at the same distance apart, the instrument can be programmed to give a direct readout in FPS as well as other information such as average values of velocity or energy. They are very easy to use and are especially handy when working in the home workshop provided that a suitably safe backstop is positioned to catch the pellets. However, since the size of the tube is not very large, the instrument is limited to the measurement of velocities at or near the muzzle, unless of course the unit is well protected while down range figures are obtained.

The second system is usually more costly, and except in the very expensive models it only gives a readout in time, this must later be converted into velocity. They are more versatile in their application because the pellet is not constrained to flying over a small sensitive area. Indeed, in conditions of suitable light, successful readings may be obtained when the pellet flies ten inches or so above the unit. Of course it is very importance that the two screens are accurately positioned at the predetermined distance apart, this dimension is of utmost importance in the calculation of the velocity.

The equation for converting the readout into velocity is:

Velocity = Skyscreen Spacing (**D**istance) x Time base speed
Chrono Readout (**T**ime)

The Sky Screen chrono is especially effective when studying the ballistic characteristics of pellets, because as we have already seen in Chapter 19 velocity reading must be taken at distances down range, at this distance the placing of a pellet safely inside the tube of a single unit chrono is not always guaranteed.

One of the most important aspects of any chrono system is that it must either work correctly or not at all, some instruments have a self checking facility built into them which allows all the functions to be monitored at the press of a button. Most chronos are designed to operate on either mains power or a battery, if the battery power is too low to give correct readings there must be an indicator to show that the battery can no longer cope and must be exchanged.

The prime purpose of chronos has always been to obtain velocity figures for research, or for the benefit of the user of the ammunition. All the chronos on the market today are capable of producing figures which are more than adequate for these requirements. However, in Britain the velocity indicated by a chrono has legal implications also, our airguns are exempt from licensing regulations only if their power is below a certain limit, in the case of a rifle it must not be capable of exceeding 12 Ft.Lbs. muzzle energy, while a pistol must not be capable of exceeding 6 Ft. Lbs.

This legal restriction on muzzle energy means that privately owned chronos must be as accurate as those employed by the authorities. This situation leads to the thorny question of checking the calibration of these instruments, to which there seems to be no satisfactory answer. In electronic terms it is very easy to check each section of a chrono's circuitry for accuracy. However from the optical point of view it is difficult to determine the exact moment at which the projectile is actually *"seen"* by the instrument. If for some physical reason the pellet does not break each of the beams at the same position, then the distance dictated by their mechanical positioning is not correct and the figure displayed will be wrong. The error produced by this misalignment is magnified as the distance between the beams is decreased. It is for this reason that it is always advisable to place individual sky screens not less than about two feet apart. It is also vitally important that both screens are "looking" vertically upwards and are perfectly parallel with each other.

When we check a chrono for accuracy we put it in front of another of accepted reliability, we then shoot through both of them at a variety of velocities. Having noted the velocities we interchange the two chronos and repeat the process; by this procedure we are in a position to judge the accuracy of the chrono under test. Of course this system only compares the suspect chrono with one that may have errors of its own therefore the whole test must be conducted with this fact in mind.

Although there are institutions which are capable of measuring most things to the last degree of decimals, none of them have yet developed a system whereby chronos may be tested against a known standard. However, the instruments available today are easily capable of measuring to within a few feet per second. Which is legally adequate, especially when one considers that most cases coming before the courts in which an over powerful rifle is concerned, usually stem from a far more serious offence.

Chapter 21 - The Measurement of Velocity

Chapter 22
THE FUTURE

Airguns have had an interesting and varied past, their future is likely to be even more fascinating. From our first serious contact with them in about 1967 we could see that in a changing world true firearms were becoming less acceptable through noise and overpopulation, therefore the acceptance of airguns in their various forms could only increase. Inevitably they will become even more socially acceptable in the future, not only with the general public but also those who, like ourselves, are born with the instinct to shoot.

Over the last thirty years there have been huge advances in the design and construction of rifles and handguns, probably the most significant advance being the introduction of the pre-charged pneumatic system in its various forms.

Our own research has had to be carried out on a very limited budget, we have had to build most of the equipment ourselves - or borrow it, this has severely limited the depth of our investigations. Probably the most important subject for future study is that of pellet flight; the pellets currently available have a very high drag factor which limits their effective range. Pellet technology is an area which has in the past been sadly neglected by ammunition makers, the existing diabolo shape has been the undisputed standard for too long and is not now in keeping with our highly developed rifles. In our own case the lack of a wind tunnel which could provide a velocity in the region of 700 FPS limited our investigations considerably, at the low velocity of 130 FPS achievable in our small tunnel it was very difficult to determine the variation in drag between different shaped pellets of the same calibre, or to evaluate any slight modifications to an accepted round.

We have discussed amongst ourselves the construction of a spring rifle built around a clear glass cylinder. This, together with high speed photography, could reveal many further secrets of the *four phases*. A test rig built around such a cylinder, powered by a gas ram, whose power could be altered easily, would give an enormous insight into the very fast, almost instantaneous airflow encountered in rifles; especially if it was fitted with a removable transfer port, perhaps also made from glass.

Chapter 22 - The Future

CONVERSION FACTORS

Length.

1 Inch = 25.4 millimetres.
1 Foot = 12 inches. = 0.3048 metres.
1 Yard = 36 inches. = 0.33 feet. = 0.9144 metres.
1 Mile = 5280 feet. = 1760 yards. = 1.609 kilometres.
1 Millimetre = 0.0394 inch.
1 Metre = 3.281 feet. = 1.094 yards.
1 Kilometre = 1093.6 yards. = 0.621 miles.

Area.

1 Square inch = 654.2 square millimetres.
1 Square foot = 0.093 square metres.
1 Square millimetre = 0.0015 square inches.
1 Square centimetre = 0.155 square inches.
1 Square metre = 10.764 square feet.

Volume.

1 Cubic inch = 16.387 cubic centimetres.
1 Cubic centimetre = 0.061 cubic inches.

Weight.

1 Grain = 0.065 gram = 0.007 pound.
1 Pound = 7,000 grains = 0.454 kilograms.
1 Gram = 15.432 grains.
1 Kilogram = 2.205 pounds.

Work.

1 Foot pound = 1.3558 joules.
1 Joule = 0.7376 foot pounds.

Pressure.

1 Pound per square inch = 0.068046 bar. (Atmosphere)
1 Bar = 14.696 Pounds per square inch. PSI.
1 PSI = 0.0703 kilograms per square centimetre.
1 Kilogramme per square centimetre = 14.223 PSI.
1 Pascal = 1 Newton per square metre.
1 PSI = 6894.7 Pa. or 6.894 kPa.
1 Bar = 100 kPa

Velocity.

1 Foot per second = 0.3048 metres per second. = 0.682 miles per hour.
1 Mile per hour. = 1.466 FPS. = 0.447 metres per second.
1 Metre per second = 3.281 FPS = 2.237 miles per hour.

Temperature.

Centigrade to Farenheight.

$$C = \frac{5}{9} (F-32)$$

Farenheight to Centigrade.

$$F = \frac{9}{5}(C+32)$$

INDEX

Index

Index